Lesson
Assessment
Book 2
Annotated Teacher's Edition

Level 3

Mc Graw Hill **SRA**

A Division of The *McGraw-Hill* Companies

SRAonline.com

 SRA

Send all inquiries to this address:
SRA/McGraw-Hill
4400 Easton Commons
Columbus, OH 43219-6188

ISBN: 978-0-07-613093-1
MHID: 0-07-613093-2

2 3 4 5 6 7 8 9 MAZ 13 12 11 10 09 08

The *McGraw·Hill* Companies

Table of Contents

Imagine It! Lesson Assessment Books

Lesson Assessment Book 1 and *Lesson Assessment Book 2* are an integral part of a complete assessment program that aligns with the instruction in *Imagine It! Lesson Assessment Book 1* covers material from Units 1–3. *Lesson Assessment Book 2* covers material from Units 4–6. The skills featured in lesson assessments are tied to reading success and reflect both state and national standards.

Lesson Assessment Book 1 and *Lesson Assessment Book 2* offer the opportunity for summative and formative assessment. As students complete each lesson, they will be assessed on their understanding of the instructional content and the literature in each lesson. The results of the assessments will then be used to inform subsequent instruction. How students score on the assessments offers a picture of current student achievement status while also guiding you toward appropriate instructional decisions.

Each lesson assessment offers you the ability to gauge students' understanding of and growth in the following areas:

• Vocabulary
• Comprehension
• Grammar, Usage, and Mechanics
• Oral Fluency
• Writing

Lesson Assessments

The lesson assessments consist of the following:

Lesson Area	Format	Scope	Scoring
Vocabulary	Multiple Choice	Selection Vocabulary and Word Structure elements	10 points (5 questions x 2 point)
Comprehension	Multiple Choice	Comprehension Skills	5 points (5 questions x 1 point)
	Short Answer	Comprehension Skills	10 points (5 questions x 2 points)
	Linking to the Concepts (Short Answer)	General comprehension related to a selection	4 points (0-4 rubrics)
	Personal Response (Short Answer)	General comprehension related to a selection	3 points (0-3 rubrics)
	Analyzing the Selection (Extended Response)	Understanding and development of ideas about selections and the unit theme	8 points (0-8 rubrics)
Grammar, Usage, and Mechanics	Multiple Choice	Grammar, Usage, and Mechanics skills practiced in the lesson	10 points (5 questions x 2 point)
Oral Fluency	Teacher-Directed Student Performance	Oral fluency development from lesson to lesson	Accuracy Rate on 100-point scale

Students will be graded on their understanding of the vocabulary, word structure, comprehension, and grammar, usage, and mechanics skills taught in the lesson on a 50-point scale. A score of 80% (or 40 points out of 50) or higher on each lesson assessment is expected. Students may look back at the selection to answer the assessment questions. Students who consistently fall below 80% should be monitored for possible intervention. Students who are consistent low-performers in one or more aspects of the lesson assessment should be offered more practice in this lesson area during Workshop.

The Oral Fluency Assessments are scored separately. These assessments offer further data on student abilities. Student performance on oral fluency assessments is often a reliable predictor of student growth and understanding in other lesson areas. Students with consistently low accuracy rates and below-level words per minute numbers should be provided extra fluency practice during Workshop.

End of Unit Writing Prompt

Over the course of the year, students will encounter six writing prompts, two each in the narrative, expository, and persuasive genres. These prompts reflect students' prior knowledge and experience with writing to a specific genre. Each prompt consists of a writing situation, a specific audience, directions for writing, and a checklist students can reference to ensure they receive the best score possible. Rubrics for scoring student work follow each prompt in this book. These rubrics pertain to genre, writing traits, and conventions. Students will be graded on a 20-point scale based on the rubrics—four points multiplied by five key writing features.

A score of 75% (or 15 points out of 20) or higher on each writing prompt is expected. Students can respond to the prompts in their student workbooks.

Scores and Records

The opening page of each lesson assessment includes a place for students to write their names and the date, and for you to list their scores.

The Oral Fluency Assessment includes a box in which to write the accuracy rate.

The writing prompt includes a place for students to write their names and the date, and for you to list their scores.

Students' scores in the assessment can be registered in the Oral Fluency Scores, Class Assessment Record, and Student Assessment Record pages.

Lesson Assessment Sections

Students may look back at the selection to answer the assessment questions.

Vocabulary

Each vocabulary assessment is comprised of five multiple-choice questions worth two points each. Four of the questions feature selection vocabulary words from the lesson students have just completed. The remaining question in the assessment pertains to a word structure element from that lesson. The format of this question varies based on the word structure feature that is being assessed.

Comprehension: Multiple Choice

Each comprehension assessment begins with five multiple-choice questions worth one point each. The items reflect the comprehension skills students have been taught specifically in that lesson and skills students have been previously taught.

Comprehension: Short Answer

Next, students answer five short-answer questions worth two points each. These questions also reflect comprehension skills specific to the lesson and to students' prior knowledge and understanding of comprehension skills. Well-crafted and concise responses that answer the question fully should be awarded two points. Answers that partially address the question or are confusing and incomplete should be awarded a point, at your discretion. Answers that do not attempt to address the question or provide incorrect information should receive zero points.

Please note the "Possible answers below" following the directions in this Teacher's Edition. This serves as a reminder that students do not have to provide the exact answer shown, and that in some cases more than one answer is possible. For example, questions that ask for "one reason" or "one example" of something might be answered by a reason or example not specified in this Teacher's Edition.

Comprehension: Linking to the Concepts

In this section, students craft a response to a question related to the selection they have just read. These questions do not focus on a particular comprehension skill; rather, they assess general comprehension of a selection by focusing on a key element in a selection which students should be comfortable identifying and writing to or about. These questions are worth four points each. Use the following criteria to judge student responses. To fully answer the question or prompt, student answers should be approximately thirty to sixty words.

Score: 4
The student understands the question and responds using information from the selection. The response is correct, reflects a thorough comprehension of the selection, and is an acceptably complete answer to the question. The organization of the response is meaningful, it is written smoothly, and sentences flow together. The response focuses on the topic. If multiple paragraphs are written, they are linked to one another with effective transitions. The response reads easily and demonstrates a sense of audience. It has correct spelling, grammar, usage, and mechanics, and it is written neatly and legibly.

Score: 3
The student understands the question and responds using information from the selection. The response may reflect comprehension of the selection and is a somewhat complete answer to the question. The organization of the response is meaningful, it is written smoothly, and sentences flow together. The response focuses on the topic. If multiple paragraphs are written, they are linked to one another with effective transitions. The response reads easily and demonstrates a sense of audience. It has occasional errors in spelling, grammar, usage, and mechanics, and it is mostly written neatly and legibly.

Score: 2
The student has partial understanding of the question. The response may reflect limited comprehension of the selection and is an incomplete answer to the question. The organization of the response is weak, it is written carelessly, and sentences are somewhat disorganized. The response includes extraneous information. If multiple paragraphs are written, they are linked to one another ineffectively. The response requires some effort to read easily and demonstrates a poor sense of audience. It has occasional errors in spelling, grammar, usage, and mechanics, and it is written somewhat neatly and legibly.

Score: 1
The student has minimal understanding of the question. The response may reflect poor comprehension of the selection and is a barely acceptable answer to the question. The organization of the response is imprecise, it is written erratically, and sentences may be disjointed. The response is poorly focused. If multiple paragraphs are written, they are linked to one another inconsistently. The response is difficult to follow and may cause the reader to struggle. It has frequent errors in spelling, grammar, usage, and mechanics, and it is written with borderline neatness and legibility.

Score: 0

The student fails to compose a response. If a response is attempted, it is inaccurate, meaningless, or irrelevant. The response may be written so poorly that it is neither legible nor understandable.

The following is an example of a response that would receive a score of "4" if it were written neatly and legibly. The student shows an understanding of the question and relates information pertaining to the selection. The answer is organized, and the sections of the response relate to one another. There are no errors in spelling, grammar, usage, and mechanics. This is an exemplary response.

SAMPLE

Linking to the Concepts *How do you think Rosie felt when she saw her old family at the graduation?*

Rosie was probably happy, but she didn't show it. She didn't do anything because she was trained well. She probably wanted to jump around and lick them, but she didn't. She needed to be by her new person.

Comprehension: Personal Response

In this section, students are asked to craft a personal response related to an idea or thematic issue raised by the selection they have just read. This section judges students' level of comprehension by assessing their ability to connect what they have just read to a personal level.

These questions are worth three points each. Use the following criteria to judge student responses. To fully answer the question or prompt, student answers should be approximately thirty to sixty words.

Score: 3

The student understands the question and responds suitably using a personal experience, opinion, prior knowledge, or plausible conjecture. The response reflects a thorough comprehension of the selection and is an acceptably complete answer to the question. The organization of the response is meaningful, it is written smoothly, and sentences flow together. The response focuses on the topic. If multiple paragraphs are written, they are linked to one another with effective transitions. The response reads easily and demonstrates a sense of audience. It has correct spelling, grammar, usage, and mechanics, and it is written neatly and legibly.

Score: 2

The student understands the question and responds using a personal experience, opinion, prior knowledge, or plausible conjecture. The response may reflect partial comprehension of the selection and is a somewhat complete answer to the question. The organization of the response is imprecise, it is written erratically, and sentences may be somewhat disjointed. The response is not clearly focused. If multiple paragraphs are written, they are linked to one another ineffectively. The response is difficult to follow and demonstrates little awareness of the reader. It has a moderate number of errors in spelling, grammar, usage, and mechanics, and it is mostly written neatly and legibly.

Score: 1

The student has minimal understanding of the question and responds using a personal experience, opinion, prior knowledge, or plausible conjecture. The response may reflect poor comprehension of the selection and is a barely acceptable answer to the question. The organization of the response is imprecise, it is written erratically, and sentences may be disjointed. The response is poorly focused. If multiple paragraphs are written, they are linked to one another inconsistently. The response is difficult to follow and may cause the reader to struggle. It has frequent errors in spelling, grammar, usage, and mechanics, and it is written with borderline neatness and legibility.

Score: 0

The student fails to compose a response. If a response is attempted, it is inaccurate, meaningless, or irrelevant. The response may be written so poorly that it is neither legible nor understandable.

The following is an example of a response that would receive a score of "1" if it were written with borderline neatness and legibility. The student shows some understanding of the question. However, the response begins and ends abruptly, the reader has to guess the type of store, there is little explanation of what would be done to get people to come to the store, and there are errors in spelling and grammar.

SAMPLE

Personal Response *What kind of business would you like to open? How would you get people to come to your business?*

It would be a nice store with lots of things. People would come because the cloths would be nice and from teams like pros and colleges. It would things that girls would like and boys.

Grammar, Usage, and Mechanics

Each grammar, usage, and mechanics assessment is comprised of five multiple-choice questions worth two points each. Each question specifically relates to the lesson material for that week. Students sometimes will be asked to identify errors or incorrect constructions, so remind students to read each question carefully.

Comprehension: Analyzing the Selection

This section of the assessment allows students to craft a longer, more detailed response to show their comprehension of what they have read. It also provides additional data on the writing skills of students as they progress through the program.

Students will sometimes be asked to respond by connecting the selection they have just read to previous selections in the unit.

These questions and prompts are worth eight points each. Use the following criteria to judge student responses. To fully answer the question or prompt, student answers should be approximately ninety to one hundred and thirty words.

Note: You will notice that the rubrics below each have a two-point range. Use your professional judgment in awarding the higher point total in the scale to students' work.

Score: 8 or 7

The student understands the question and responds suitably using the appropriate source of information. These sources include the selection itself, other selections, personal experience, opinion, prior knowledge, or plausible conjecture. The response reflects a thorough comprehension of the selection and is an acceptably complete answer to the question. The organization of the response is meaningful, it is written smoothly, and both sentences and paragraphs flow together. Paragraphs focus on related topics and are linked to one another with effective transitions. The response reads easily and demonstrates a sense of audience. It has correct spelling, grammar, usage, and mechanics, and it is written neatly and legibly.

Score: 6 or 5

The student understands the question and responds suitably using the appropriate source of information. These sources include the selection itself, other selections, personal experience, opinion, prior knowledge, or plausible conjecture. The response may reflect comprehension of the selection or other sources and is a somewhat complete answer to the question. The organization of the response is somewhat meaningful, and both sentences and paragraphs flow together relatively smoothly. Paragraphs focus on related topics and are linked to one another with effective transitions. The response reads easily and demonstrates a sense of audience. It has occasional errors in spelling, grammar, usage, and mechanics, and it is written somewhat neatly and legibly.

Score: 4 or 3

The student has partial understanding of the question. The response may reflect limited comprehension of the selection and is an incomplete answer to the question or includes irrelevant information. The organization of the response is weak, it is written carelessly, and both sentences and paragraphs are somewhat disorganized. Paragraphs include some extraneous information and are linked to one another ineffectively. The response requires some effort to read easily and demonstrates a poor sense of audience. It has occasional errors in spelling, grammar, usage, and mechanics, and it is written somewhat neatly and legibly.

Score: 2 or 1

The student has minimal understanding of the question. The response may reflect poor comprehension of the selection and is a barely acceptable answer to the question or includes irrelevant information. The organization of the response is imprecise, it is written erratically, and sentences or paragraphs may be disjointed. Paragraphs may be poorly focused or are linked to one another inconsistently. The response is difficult to follow and may cause the reader to struggle. It has frequent errors in spelling, grammar, usage, and mechanics, and it is written with borderline neatness and legibility.

Score: 0

The student fails to compose a response. If a response is attempted, it is inaccurate, meaningless, or irrelevant. The response may be written so poorly that it is neither legible nor understandable.

The following is an example of a response that would receive a score of "2" if written with borderline neatness and legibility. The student does show an understanding of the question. However, the response is written erratically and has few real details and little support. There are many errors in spelling, grammar, usage, and mechanics.

SAMPLE

Analyzing the Selection *There are different kinds of selections in this unit. What are some of the things you enjoyed about each selection?*

The Tomás story was good because the library lade was nice to Tomás. Liberians are pretty nice, so the story was kind of true.

Big Wind wasn't very good. I didn't like it alot. The storm store was good because they had fun even though the electricity was off. The cat was good even though it was afraid.

The pottery story was okay. It was neat how the old people taught the children about making pots. I didn't think the story was real, but we talked about it in class and some people live like that even today.

The Johnny Appleseed story I knew from before. My uncle told me about it. I think the story is true that there was a real Jonny Appleseed. There are apple trees all over so. somebody had to plant them

Oral Fluency Assessments

Administering Oral Fluency Assessments

The Oral Fluency Assessment is an efficient means for evaluating students' ability to read. It is simple to administer and score, yet it provides extraordinarily useful quantitative and qualitative data. You will find oral fluency assessments for each lesson. The words in the selections are of sufficient variety to allow for an analysis of the decoding and vocabulary abilities of a student and to draw inferences about a student's ability to derive meaning from the text.

Make a copy of the Oral Fluency Assessment for each student you will be assessing. Have students turn to the corresponding page in their workbooks. Be sure you have a pen or pencil, a stopwatch or other timer, and extra paper to record any observations. Briefly review the text before you begin. On the Oral Fluency Scores pages, you will record the student's name, the date of the assessment, and the results of the assessment.

Have the student sit comfortably at a table with you. Seat yourself and the student so that you can mark the assessment unobtrusively without distracting the student.

Say: *Here is a selection I would like you to read aloud for me. I am going to listen to you read and take some notes. The notes I take will help me learn how well you can read. You will not be graded for this, so you should not feel nervous. Read the selection carefully and do your best. Take a few minutes now to look over the selection, and then I will tell you when to begin.*

Allow time for the student to preview the story. Be sure you have a pen or pencil.

Say: *Are you ready?* (Check to be sure the student is ready.) *You may begin now.*

Start the timer or watch as the student begins to read. You may pronounce any proper nouns with which the student is unfamiliar. Do not count these words as errors.

Note: If the student becomes frustrated or makes several consecutive errors, stop the assessment.

At the end of one minute place a bracket ( ]) at the end of the last word the student reads.

Scoring Oral Fluency Assessments

The following guidelines will help you score the assessment accurately and consistently.

- Self-correcting should not be counted as an error.
- Repeating the same mistake should be counted as only one error.
- Hesitating for more than five seconds—at which point you would have provided the word—should count as an error.
- Become familiar with the evaluating codes before administering the Oral Fluency Assessment.

Scoring Conventions

- Draw a line through any word that is misread. Count this as an error. If possible, note the type of error. (Misreading *short a* as *short e*, reading *get* as *jet*, and so on).
- Draw a bracket ( ]) at the end of the last word the student reads in one minute.
- Words the student omits should be counted as errors, even if you prompt the student.
- Indicate with a caret extra words that have been inserted. If possible, write the inserted word. Count insertions as errors.
- Draw an arrow between words that have been reversed. Count these as one error.
- Students might repeat words on occasion. Do not count this behavior as an error.

Finding the Student's Accuracy Rate

To find a student's accuracy rate, count the total number of words read in one minute. The numbers beside the passage on the teacher's page will make this an easier task. Subtract the number of errors from the total number of words read and use that figure to find the number of correct words read per minute. Then divide the correct words per minute by the total number of words read to find the accuracy rate. Record these numbers on the Reading Rate and Accuracy chart located on your Oral Fluency Assessment pages.

- Record the student's score on the Oral Fluency Scores pages and the Student Assessment Record.
- Complete the Reading Fluency scale at the bottom of your Oral Fluency Assessment page. These qualitative measures indicate your subjective judgment of how the student compares with other students who are reading at grade level.

READING RATE AND ACCURACY

Total Words Read:	130
Number of Errors:	19
Number of Correct Words Read Per Minute (WPM):	111
Accuracy Rate:	85%

(Number of Correct Words Read per Minute ÷ Total Words Read)

READING FLUENCY

	Low	Average	High
Decoding Ability	○	○	●
Pace	○	●	○
Syntax	○	●	○
Self-correction	○	●	○
Intonation	○	○	●

Interpreting the Oral Fluency Assessments

First, compare the student's number of correct words per minute with the following chart. This will give you an idea of how the student compares with other students in the same grade at the same time of year. The data in this chart represents the approximate number of correct words read per minute a student should be reading in Grades 2–6. The two rows of numbers represent the 50th and 75th percentiles.

	Units 1-2	Units 3-4	Units 5-6	
Grade 2	79	100	117	75th Percentile
	51	72	89	50th Percentile
Grade 3	99	120	137	75th Percentile
	71	92	107	50th Percentile
Grade 4	119	139	152	75th Percentile
	94	112	123	50th Percentile
Grade 5	139	156	168	75th Percentile
	110	127	139	50th Percentile
Grade 6	153	167	177	75th Percentile
	127	140	150	50th Percentile

Source Adapted from Hasbrouck, J., & Tindal, G. (2005). Oral Reading Fluency: 90 Years of Measurement (Tech. Rep. No. 33). Eugene, Oregon: University of Oregon, College of Education, Behavioral Research and Teaching.

Then examine the student's accuracy rate. Reading accuracy should remain constant or gradually increase within a grade and between grades, until it stabilizes at ninety percent or higher. You may find it helpful to compare a student's accuracy rate after each administration to ensure that it remains constant or increases.

Next, examine the types of errors the student is making and consider how they represent underlying student behaviors. Here are some examples:

- Inserting extra words suggests that the student understands what is read, is constructing meaning, but is reading somewhat impulsively.

- A student who refuses to attempt to read a word is probably uncertain of his or her abilities and is unwilling to take risks.

- Misreading regular letter sounds implies that the student has not yet mastered the conventions of the sound-symbol relationship. This is in contrast with the student who misreads complex letter sounds (alternate sounds, blends, diphthongs, digraphs, and so on) but has little difficulty with regular letter sounds.

Finally, consider the error pattern. If errors are scattered randomly throughout the passage, then the error types represent skills the student has not yet developed. If errors increase in frequency from beginning to end, then fatigue or inattention likely are involved.

Other Considerations

Several strategies are available for promoting reading fluency and accuracy. These involve pairing an accomplished reader with a developing reader, small-group choral reading, and repeated readings of familiar text.

You may find it useful to establish targets for reading accuracy. These targets may include goals such as reading ten words in a row without error, increasing by increments the number of correct words a student reads in a minute, or decreasing a specific error type. Establishing such targets allows you to provide appropriate instructional support and gives students a reasonable goal.

End of Unit Writing Prompt

The writing prompt offers the opportunity for an on-demand writing performance similar to the type students will encounter in high-stakes testing. Use the rubrics that follow the prompts to judge students' work. Student writing should be included in each student's Writing Portfolio.

Teacher Records

This Teacher's Edition contains record keeping material that will help you keep track of student progress in lesson assessments.

Six Point Rubrics

Six Point Writing Rubrics for assessing student writing are included.

These can take the place of the four point rubrics if you are in a school that uses the six point rubric system.

Oral Fluency Scores

These pages allow you to note student accuracy rates throughout the year.

Class Assessment Record

These pages offer a warehouse for class scores.

The spaces following the student's name allow for the recording of student scores in each lesson assessment (out of the 50-point scale) and each writing prompt (using the four point or six point rubrics to assess).

The format of the Class Assessment Record provides an easy way to monitor student growth across the year.

Student Assessment Record

You can duplicate this page for each student and use it to track student progress.

Comprehension Observation Log

Observing students as they read anthology selections is an effective way to learn their strengths and areas of need in comprehension. Use the Comprehension Observation Log to record your observations of students. Choose a small set of students to focus on for a particular lesson. You might want to observe students more than once to get a clear idea of their comprehension of texts. Copy this page for each student or group of students you observe.

Name _____ Date _____ Score _____

Sun

Vocabulary

Read each item. Fill in the bubble for the answer you think is correct.

1. Which suffix means "action" or "process"?

Ⓐ -ly   Ⓒ -y

Ⓑ -ment   Ⓓ -ed

2. Slightly means

Ⓐ a little.   Ⓒ hotly.

Ⓑ slowly.   Ⓓ a bunch.

3. The sun rises and sets on the **horizon.** The **horizon** is

Ⓐ a line that goes straight up like a flagpole.

Ⓑ a line around the center of another planet.

Ⓒ a line where sky and ground seem to meet.

Ⓓ a line that reaches from the sun to the Earth.

4. The path of Earth around the sun is an **oval.** An **oval** is shaped like

Ⓐ an apple.   Ⓒ a flag.

Ⓑ a box.   Ⓓ an egg.

5. Earth's **orbit** goes around the sun. What is Earth's **orbit?**

Ⓐ its path around the sun

Ⓑ the way it turns on its axis

Ⓒ its place near other planets

Ⓓ its path around the moon

Sun (continued)

Comprehension

Read the following questions carefully. Then completely fill in the bubble of each correct answer. You may look back at the selection to find the answer to each of the questions.

1. The sun is a

    Ⓐ planet.

    Ⓑ comet.

    Ⓒ cloud.

    Ⓓ star.

2. Which of these is true about the sun?

    Ⓐ It is too close to Earth.

    Ⓑ It is made mostly of metal.

    Ⓒ It is too hot to live there.

    Ⓓ It is the same size as Earth.

Sun (continued)

3. Bursts of hot gas that shoot out from the sun are called
   Ⓐ sunspots.
   Ⓑ solar storms.
   Ⓒ solar flares.
   Ⓓ electrical patches.

4. The sun is the center of
   Ⓐ the solar system.
   Ⓑ the universe.
   Ⓒ the horizon.
   Ⓓ the sunspot storms.

5. Earth has seasons because
   Ⓐ it is far from the sun.
   Ⓑ it is tilted a little.
   Ⓒ there are other planets.
   Ⓓ there are other stars.

Sun (continued)

Read the following questions carefully. Use complete sentences to answer the questions. Possible answers below

6. Why does the sun look larger than the stars in the night sky?

The sun is much closer to Earth than any other stars, so it looks larger.

7. Why should you not look right at the sun?

You can hurt your eyes if you look at the sun for even a few seconds.

8. How do scientists study the sun?

They put filters on their telescopes and use cameras to take pictures.

9. What might cause the dark spots on the sun?

These spots may be giant storms. The darkness is due to low temperatures.

10. How does the sun help Earth?

It gives Earth warmth and light so people, animals, and plants can grow and live.

Sun (continued)

Read the question below. Write complete sentences for your answer. Support your answer with information from the selection.

Linking to the Concepts Is the sun burning? Explain your answer.

_____

_____

_____

_____

_____

Read the question below. Your answer should be based on your own experience. Write complete sentences for your answer.

Personal Response Do you like the long days of summer or the short days of winter? Explain your answer.

_____

_____

_____

_____

_____

Sun (continued)

Grammar, Usage, and Mechanics

Read each question. Fill in the bubble beside the answer in each group that is correct. If none of the answers is correct, choose the last answer, "none of the above."

1. Which sentence has correct punctuation?

Ⓐ Yes you may go.   Ⓒ Yes, you may go.

Ⓑ Yes, you, may go.   Ⓓ none of the above

2. Which sentence has correct punctuation?

Ⓐ You can eat, sleep, and relax here.

Ⓑ You can eat sleep, and relax here.

Ⓒ You can eat sleep and relax here.

Ⓓ none of the above

3. Which sentence has correct punctuation?

Ⓐ No I haven't eaten.   Ⓒ No, I haven't eaten

Ⓑ No I haven't, eaten.   Ⓓ none of the above

4. Which sentence has correct punctuation?

Ⓐ Mia bought a new sofa, chair, and table.

Ⓑ Mia bought a new sofa chair, and table.

Ⓒ Mia bought a new, sofa, chair and table.

Ⓓ none of the above

5. Which sentence has a mistake in punctuation?

Ⓐ Yes, dinner is almost ready.

Ⓑ We will have fish, potatoes, and a salad.

Ⓒ No we, will not be having desert.

Ⓓ none of the above

Sun (continued)

Analyzing the Selection

Read the question below. Write complete sentences for your answer. Support your answer with information from the selection.

What does it mean to say that the sun is the center of our neighborhood in space?

_____

_____

_____

_____

_____

_____

_____

_____

_____

_____

_____

_____

_____

Sun (continued)

Oral Fluency Assessment

A Special Flag

Our flag has many different names. Some people call it "Old
Glory." But that is really the name for one special flag. This flag
has an unusual story.

In 1831, a mother made a large American flag for her son. He
was a sea captain. His name was William Driver, and he flew
the flag on his boat. When it flew, he called it a name. He called
it "Old Glory."

Years later, he stopped sailing. He moved to the South. Now
his flag flew from his house.

During the Civil War, the South left the union. People
fighting for the South came to Driver's home. They wanted to
take the flag.

But they could not find it. The flag stayed hidden until 1862.
Then the Union Army took over the city.

Driver went home. He opened up his bed cover. There was
his flag! He had kept it safe during the war.

After he hung the flag in town, newspapers heard about it.
They wrote about this special flag. Soon it became famous all
over the country.

1–11
12–24
25–28
29–41
42–53
54–68
69–71
72–82
83–88
89–98
99–109
110–112
113–124
125–132
133–143
144–153
154–164
165–175
176–178

**EVALUATING CODES
FOR ORAL FLUENCY**

sky   (/) words read incorrectly

blue
 ^ sky   (^) inserted word
          ( ]) after the last word

READING RATE AND ACCURACY

Total Words Read: _____

Number of Errors: _____

Number of Correct Words
Read Per Minute (WPM):   _____

Accuracy Rate: _____

(Number of Correct Words Read per
Minute ÷ Total Words Read)

READING FLUENCY

	Low	Average	High
Decoding ability	○	○	○
Pace	○	○	○
Syntax	○	○	○
Self-correction	○	○	○
Intonation	○	○	○

Record student rates on the Oral Fluency Scores pages.

Name _____ Date _____ Score _____

Grandmother Spider Brings the Sun

Vocabulary

Read each item. Fill in the bubble for the answer you think is correct.

1. Clay is

- Ⓐ sticky mud.
- Ⓒ warm water.
- Ⓑ hard rock.
- Ⓓ green grass.

2. What does *careful* mean?

- Ⓐ too little care
- Ⓒ full of care
- Ⓑ made of care
- Ⓓ without care

3. The animals planned to **sneak** to the sun. This means they were going to

- Ⓐ run as quickly as they could.
- Ⓑ go in a big group and stay together.
- Ⓒ dig slowly through the earth.
- Ⓓ go quietly without being seen.

4. The animals asked Wolf for **directions** in the dark. They needed to know

- Ⓐ what they bumped into.
- Ⓑ which way to go.
- Ⓒ what time it was.
- Ⓓ who their friends were.

5. Possum's eyes got **squinty.** This means his eyes were

- Ⓐ wide open.
- Ⓒ wet with tears.
- Ⓑ partly closed.
- Ⓓ rolling around.

Grandmother Spider Brings the Sun (continued)

Comprehension

**Read the following questions carefully. Then completely
fill in the bubble of each correct answer. You may look
back at the selection to find the answer to each of
the questions.**

1. Which of these happened first when Possum got to
   the other side?

   Ⓐ He took a piece of sun.

   Ⓑ He rubbed his eyes with his dirty fists.

   Ⓒ His eyes had rings around them.

   Ⓓ He was blinded by the light.

2. What did Grandmother Spider use to bring back light?

   Ⓐ a large web

   Ⓑ a long string

   Ⓒ a clay bowl

   Ⓓ black feathers

Grandmother Spider Brings the Sun (continued)

3. This folktale is written from the

Ⓐ first-person point of view of Possum.

Ⓑ second-person point of view.

Ⓒ third-person point of view.

Ⓓ first-person point of view of Wolf.

4. The purpose of this folktale is to

Ⓐ show that spiders are good at stealing.

Ⓑ explain how animals help each other.

Ⓒ show that possums are not very smart.

Ⓓ explain how the sun got into the sky.

5. You know this folktale cannot be realistic because

Ⓐ the spider is tiny.

Ⓑ the animals talk.

Ⓒ the possum had sharp claws.

Ⓓ the buzzard had feathers.

UNIT 4 Lesson 2

Grandmother Spider Brings the Sun (continued)

Read the following questions carefully. Use complete sentences to answer the questions. Possible answers below

6. Why did everyone ask Wolf for directions?

There was no light. The other animals couldn't see in the dark, but Wolf could.

7. How were Wolf's and Coyote's plans for getting a piece of sun different?

Wolf wanted to ask for the piece, but Coyote said they should steal it.

8. Why did the animals not have light after Possum came back?

Possum hid the sun under his tail. When he came back, his tail was burning. The others put it out with water.

9. How did Buzzard feel after he returned with the sun?

He was embarrassed; the little piece of sun on his head made him bald.

10. In what order did the three animals go to the sun?

Possum went first, Buzzard was second, and Grandmother Spider went last.

UNIT 4 **Lesson 2**

Grandmother Spider Brings the Sun (continued)

Read the question below. Write complete sentences for your answer. Support your answer with information from the selection.

Linking to the Concepts Why did Grandmother Spider's plan work better than the other animals' ideas?

_____

_____

_____

_____

_____

Read the questions below. Your answer should be based on your own experience. Write complete sentences for your answer.

Personal Response Which animal did you find most interesting? Why did you find this animal interesting?

_____

_____

_____

_____

_____

Grandmother Spider Brings the Sun (continued)

Grammar, Usage, and Mechanics

Read each question. Fill in the bubble beside the answer in each group that is correct. If none of the answers is correct, choose the last answer, "none of the above."

1. Which of these is a compound word?

- Ⓐ adventure
- Ⓑ football
- Ⓒ curious
- Ⓓ none of the above

2. Which of these is a contraction?

- Ⓐ friends'
- Ⓑ crowd's
- Ⓒ wasn't
- Ⓓ none of the above

3. Which of these compound words is "something that digs in the ground"?

- Ⓐ handmade
- Ⓒ earthworm
- Ⓑ doorknob
- Ⓓ none of the above

4. What is another way to write the words <u>you will</u>?

- Ⓐ you've
- Ⓒ you're
- Ⓑ you'll
- Ⓓ none of the above

5. What does the contraction <u>weren't</u> stand for?

- Ⓐ were not
- Ⓒ worn out
- Ⓑ we are
- Ⓓ none of the above

Grandmother Spider Brings the Sun (continued)

Analyzing the Selection

Read the questions below. Write complete sentences for your answer. Support your answer with information from the selection.

Why were the animals willing to help Grandmother Spider? Why was she willing to help the other animals? Use information from the selection and your own opinion.

_____

_____

_____

_____

_____

_____

_____

_____

_____

_____

_____

_____

Grandmother Spider Brings the Sun (continued)

Oral Fluency Assessment

Birdwatcher

Many schools now have small nature areas. Most of these have a bird feeder of some kind. If your school has a feeder, try this.

Find a spot that is close enough to the feeder to see the birds. Do not get so close that you scare them away.

During the day, keep a record of the birds that are at the feeder. Write the type of bird. List how many there are of each kind. If possible, watch the feeder at the same time each day.

Create a list of birds that appear at the feeder. Make a wall chart with the name of each bird that appears at the feeder. In addition, keep a detailed notebook showing what the birds were doing.

This activity can lead to other projects. You can keep a list of birds on a computer. You can also study bird families. You can find out the times of the day that are best for observing types of birds. You might even be able to explain why this happens.

| 1–10 |
| 11–23 |
| 24–25 |
| 26–39 |
| 40–49 |
| 50–62 |
| 63–75 |
| 76–87 |
| 88–100 |
| 101–112 |
| 113–122 |
| 123–124 |
| 125–137 |
| 138–149 |
| 150–162 |
| 163–174 |

**EVALUATING CODES
FOR ORAL FLUENCY**

sky   (/) words read incorrectly

blue
  ^   sky   (^) inserted word
               ( ]) after the last word

READING RATE AND ACCURACY

Total Words Read: _____

Number of Errors: _____

Number of Correct Words
Read Per Minute (WPM): _____

Accuracy Rate: _____

(Number of Correct Words Read per
Minute ÷ Total Words Read)

READING FLUENCY

	Low	Average	High
Decoding ability	○	○	○
Pace	○	○	○
Syntax	○	○	○
Self-correction	○	○	○
Intonation	○	○	○

Record student rates on the Oral Fluency Scores pages.

Name _____ Date _____ Score _____

The Moon Seems to Change

Vocabulary

Read each item. Fill in the bubble for the answer you think is correct.

1. What does the suffix **-less** mean?

Ⓐ made of   Ⓒ without

Ⓑ action   Ⓓ state of

2. Phases is another word for

Ⓐ sounds.   Ⓒ stages.

Ⓑ skies.   Ⓓ lights.

3. A **crescent moon** can be seen on some nights. A **crescent moon** can best be described as

Ⓐ a curved shape. Ⓒ a half circle.

Ⓑ a triangle.   Ⓓ a full circle.

4. Sometimes the moon is just a **sliver.** A **sliver** is a

Ⓐ bright, wide stripe.

Ⓑ big, round circle.

Ⓒ colorful rectangle.

Ⓓ thin, narrow piece.

5. A **new moon** describes when the moon

Ⓐ is round and full.

Ⓑ cannot be seen.

Ⓒ has gotten larger.

Ⓓ is a half circle.

The Moon Seems to Change (continued)

Comprehension

Read the following questions carefully. Then completely fill in the bubble of each correct answer. You may look back at the selection to find the answer to each of the questions.

1. Why does the moon seem to change size?

Ⓐ Earth turns so the moon cannot be seen most nights.

Ⓑ Clouds block part of the moon some nights.

Ⓒ The sun is not as bright sometimes, so the moon fades.

Ⓓ The moon goes around Earth, so different parts show.

2. Which of these is seen first after the new moon?

Ⓐ crescent moon

Ⓑ full moon

Ⓒ quarter moon

Ⓓ half moon

The Moon Seems to Change (continued)

3. According to the selection, the crescent moon can be seen

   Ⓐ at sunset in the west.

   Ⓑ at midnight in the south.

   Ⓒ late at night in the north.

   Ⓓ early in the morning in the east.

4. When you cannot see the moon at all, it is called

   Ⓐ a crescent moon.

   Ⓑ a new moon.

   Ⓒ a full moon.

   Ⓓ a blue moon.

5. People found out what the back side of the moon looks like because of

   Ⓐ mirrors.

   Ⓑ telescopes.

   Ⓒ spaceships.

   Ⓓ sailing ships.

The Moon Seems to Change (continued)

Read the following questions carefully. Use complete sentences to answer the questions. Possible answers below

6. How are the full moon and the quarter moon different?

The full moon is a large circle. A quarter moon looks like half a circle.

7. What is the difference between the waxing and waning moons?

The waxing moon is growing larger; the waning moon is getting smaller.

8. How does the moon get its light?

The part of the moon that faces the sun is lit up by the sunlight.

9. How is a day on the moon different from a day on Earth?

A day on Earth is twenty-four hours. A day on the moon is about a month.

10. What causes a new moon?

When it is between Earth and the sun, the unlit half of the moon faces Earth.

The Moon Seems to Change (continued)

Read the question below. Write complete sentences for your answer. Support your answer with information from the selection.

Linking to the Concepts Why can we not see the back side of the moon from Earth?

_____

_____

_____

_____

_____

Read the questions below. Your answer should be based on your own experience. Write complete sentences for your answer.

Personal Response Which of the moon's phases do you like best? Why?

_____

_____

_____

_____

_____

_____

The Moon Seems to Change (continued)

Grammar, Usage, and Mechanics

Read each question. Fill in the bubble beside the answer in each group that is correct. If none of the answers is correct, choose the last answer, "none of the above."

1. Which of these is an adverb?

Ⓐ worry

Ⓒ brightly

Ⓑ sunny

Ⓓ none of the above

2. Which sentence contains an adverb?

Ⓐ It was hard to see clearly through the dirty window.

Ⓑ The farmer drove a tractor across the field.

Ⓒ All the tents were on sale at the outdoor store.

Ⓓ none of the above

3. In which sentence is the adverb used correctly?

Ⓐ The climbers arrived back at safely camp.

Ⓑ The safely climbers arrived back at camp.

Ⓒ The climbers arrived safely back at camp.

Ⓓ none of the above

4. Which adverb tells when something happened?

Ⓐ lonely

Ⓒ sleepily

Ⓑ finally

Ⓓ none of the above

5. Which underlined adverb modifies an adjective?

Ⓐ We couldn't hear Tracy because she spoke softly.

Ⓑ Joe spilled a glass of water that was nearly full.

Ⓒ The team played badly but still won.

Ⓓ none of the above

UNIT 4 · Lesson 3

The Moon Seems to Change (continued)

Analyzing the Selection

Read the questions below. Write complete sentences for your answer. Support your answer with information from the selections.

How do the sun and moon affect Earth and its people? What would Earth be like if there were no sun or moon?

_____

_____

_____

_____

_____

_____

_____

_____

_____

_____

_____

_____

_____

The Moon Seems to Change (continued)

Oral Fluency Assessment

So Many Eggs!

The eggs you buy in the store come from female chickens, or	1–12
hens. But hens are not the only animals that make eggs. In fact,	13–25
many other animals lay eggs.	26–30
Eggs come in many sizes, just like the animals that make	31–41
them. You need two hands to hold an ostrich egg. It can weigh	42–54
up to three pounds! A hummingbird's eggs are quite small. They	55–65
are as big as your fingernail.	66–71
Animals lay their eggs in different ways, too. Some lay their	72–82
eggs one at a time. Others lay large batches of eggs at the same	83–96
time. A spider might lay hundreds of eggs in an egg sac. A frog	97–110
lays its many eggs in long strings of jelly in the water. Fish	111–123
lay groups of eggs that can either float or sink. Sea turtles fill	124–136
sandy holes with hundreds of eggs.	137–142
Eggs come in all colors, too. Chicken eggs are an example	143–153
of this. They can be white, brown, blue, or green. Animal eggs	154–165
are a fun item to study. They are as unique as the animals that	166–179
make them.	180–181

**EVALUATING CODES
FOR ORAL FLUENCY**

sky   (/) words read incorrectly

blue

 ^   sky   (^) inserted word

             ( ]) after the last word

READING RATE AND ACCURACY

Total Words Read: _____

Number of Errors: _____

Number of Correct Words
Read Per Minute (WPM):   _____

Accuracy Rate: _____

(Number of Correct Words Read per
Minute ÷ Total Words Read)

READING FLUENCY

	Low	Average	High
Decoding ability	○	○	○
Pace	○	○	○
Syntax	○	○	○
Self-correction	○	○	○
Intonation	○	○	○

Record student rates on the Oral Fluency Scores pages.

Name _____ Date _____ Score _____

Journey to the Moon

Vocabulary

Read each item. Fill in the bubble for the answer you think is correct.

1. What does the Latin root ***port*** mean?

  Ⓐ carry   Ⓒ break

  Ⓑ twist   Ⓓ hear

2. Gigantic means very

  Ⓐ fast.   Ⓒ large.

  Ⓑ slow.   Ⓓ small.

3. The moon has weak **gravity. Gravity** is a force that

  Ⓐ pushes things apart.   Ⓒ lifts things up.

  Ⓑ pulls things down.   Ⓓ stretches things out.

4. An **astronaut** is a person who

  Ⓐ studies the planets.

  Ⓑ writes about space.

  Ⓒ builds spaceships.

  Ⓓ flies in a spaceship.

5. In a space suit, **pressure** is controlled. **Pressure** is

  Ⓐ a weight that pushes against something.

  Ⓑ the average temperature.

  Ⓒ the airflow.

  Ⓓ the feeling of being tired.

Journey to the Moon (continued)

Comprehension

Read the following questions carefully. Then completely fill in the bubble of each correct answer. You may look back at the selection to find the answer to each of the questions.

1. Who was the first person to set foot on the moon?

Ⓐ Buzz Aldrin

Ⓑ Neil Armstrong

Ⓒ Michael Collins

Ⓓ Lance Aldrin

2. After the rocket had gone 240,000 miles, two of the astronauts

Ⓐ built the lunar module.

Ⓑ got ready to take off.

Ⓒ returned to Earth.

Ⓓ climbed into the lunar module.

Journey to the Moon (continued)

3. After they landed, the astronauts hopped on the moon's surface because

Ⓐ they were excited to be on the moon.

Ⓑ they had to get over bumps on the moon's surface.

Ⓒ the moon has weak gravity.

Ⓓ it was hard to walk in spacesuits.

4. How did the astronauts feel when they walked on the moon?

Ⓐ tired but excited

Ⓑ very frightened

Ⓒ lonely and sad

Ⓓ upset and angry

5. Which of these is a fact from the selection?

Ⓐ The moonwalk was important to the whole world.

Ⓑ The moon seemed empty and even a bit lonely.

Ⓒ On July 20, 1969, two men walked on the moon.

Ⓓ Everyone watching the moonwalk was excited.

Journey to the Moon (continued)

Read the following questions carefully. Use complete sentences to answer the questions. Possible answers below

6. What were the two missions that *Apollo 11* had?

Its missions were to land two men on the moon and get them back safely.

7. What were the two parts of *Apollo 11* and what did each part do?

The Columbia circled the moon, while the Eagle landed on the moon.

8. Why was the Eagle allowed to crash on the moon?

It was not needed for the trip back to Earth so it was allowed to crash.

9. Why did the astronauts plant the American flag?

The flag showed that the United States had gotten to the moon first.

10. How did Michael Collins feel as he orbited the moon? Why did he feel that way?

He was worried. He could not see or always contact the other astronauts.

Journey to the Moon (continued)

Read the question below. Write complete sentences for your answer. Support your answer with information from the selection.

Linking to the Concepts President Nixon said the world was closer together because of the moonwalk. What did he mean?

_____

_____

_____

_____

_____

Read the question below. Your answer should be based on your own experience. Write complete sentences for your answer.

Personal Response Before 1969, landing on the moon seemed impossible. What things seem impossible now that you hope will happen in the future?

_____

_____

_____

_____

_____

Journey to the Moon (continued)

Grammar, Usage, and Mechanics

Read each question. Fill in the bubble beside the answer in each group that is correct. If none of the answers is correct, choose the last answer, "none of the above."

1. Which word means about the same as <u>fight</u>?

Ⓐ costume   Ⓒ struggle

Ⓑ expect   Ⓓ none of the above

2. Which word means the opposite of <u>save</u>?

Ⓐ hose   Ⓒ growl

Ⓑ spend   Ⓓ none of the above

3. Which two words mean about the same thing?

Ⓐ nice and pleasant

Ⓑ pale and late

Ⓒ narrow and broken

Ⓓ none of the above

4. Which two words are opposites?

Ⓐ learn and hurry

Ⓑ melt and borrow

Ⓒ simple and complicated

Ⓓ none of the above

5. Which word means about the same as <u>visitor</u>?

Ⓐ stiff

Ⓑ guest

Ⓒ acorn

Ⓓ none of the above

Journey to the Moon (continued)

Analyzing the Selection

Read the questions below. Write complete sentences for your answer. Support your answer with information from the selection.

The selection says that going to the moon was "no easy task." What was the hard work involved in the mission? What were some of the dangers the astronauts faced?

_____

_____

_____

_____

_____

_____

_____

_____

_____

_____

Journey to the Moon (continued)

Oral Fluency Assessment

At the Campground

Mr. and Mrs. Cruz set up the tent. The kids were sleeping in	1–13
the back of the car. They woke the children up and helped them	14–26
into their sleeping bags.	27–30
Neither Pablo nor Linda had taken a look around the	31–40
campground before bed. This morning was their first chance to	41–50
see where they were. They were excited!	51–57
The sun rose over the top of the mountain. Fish started	58–68
breaking the surface of the nearby stream. Each time they	69–78
rose to the surface, the fish left a small ring of water. The ring	79–92
spread across the pond. As the rings bumped into one another,	93–103
they sparkled in the sunlight.	104–108
"I wonder what the fish are doing," Pablo said to Linda.	109–119
"Probably eating breakfast," answered a voice behind them.	120–127
They turned to see their mother standing right there.	128–136
Mrs. Cruz hugged the children. The three of them watched	137–146
the fish quietly for a few minutes.	147–153
"Let's head back to the tent," suggested Mrs. Cruz. "Maybe	154–163
we can convince Dad to cook. We'll need a good breakfast. We	164–175
have a busy day ahead of us."	176–182

EVALUATING CODES FOR ORAL FLUENCY

sky   (/) words read incorrectly

blue
  ^ sky   (^) inserted word
           ( ]) after the last word

READING RATE AND ACCURACY

Total Words Read: _____

Number of Errors: _____

Number of Correct Words
Read Per Minute (WPM): _____

Accuracy Rate: _____

(Number of Correct Words Read per
Minute ÷ Total Words Read)

READING FLUENCY

	Low	Average	High
Decoding ability	○	○	○
Pace	○	○	○
Syntax	○	○	○
Self-correction	○	○	○
Intonation	○	○	○

Record student rates on the Oral Fluency Scores pages.

Name _____ Date _____ Score _____

Earth

Vocabulary

Read each item. Fill in the bubble for the answer you think is correct.

1. Which Greek root means "write"?

Ⓐ *graph* Ⓒ *photo*

Ⓑ *path* Ⓓ *scope*

2. A **curve** is a line that

Ⓐ is thick. Ⓒ breaks.

Ⓑ bends. Ⓓ is colorful.

3. The **rotation** of Earth causes day and night. **Rotation** is movement

Ⓐ around a center point.

Ⓑ back and forth.

Ⓒ along an unknown path.

Ⓓ up and down.

4. **Astronomers** do not agree about Pluto. **Astronomers** are scientists who

Ⓐ fly in space ships. Ⓒ invent new rockets.

Ⓑ study stars. Ⓓ study rocks.

5. Earth has an **atmosphere. Atmosphere** means about the same as

Ⓐ severe weather. Ⓒ outer space.

Ⓑ small clouds. Ⓓ area of gas around a planet.

Earth (continued)

Comprehension

Read the following questions carefully. Then completely fill in the bubble of each correct answer. You may look back at the selection to find the answer to each of the questions.

1. Where does space start?

   Ⓐ outside the layer of air around Earth

   Ⓑ beyond all the planets and the sun

   Ⓒ where the planets begin

   Ⓓ between the planets and the sun

2. Which planet is closest to the sun?

   Ⓐ Jupiter

   Ⓑ Earth

   Ⓒ Mars

   Ⓓ Mercury

Earth (continued)

3. Why is one-half of Earth always dark?

Ⓐ The moon comes between Earth and the sun at night.

Ⓑ Clouds block the light over parts of Earth.

Ⓒ Earth spins, so half of it faces away from the sun.

Ⓓ The sun moves around Earth, so it can not always be seen.

4. When the southern half of Earth is tilted away from the sun, the southern half of Earth has

Ⓐ spring.

Ⓑ summer.

Ⓒ autumn.

Ⓓ winter.

5. All of these are true about Earth's atmosphere EXCEPT

Ⓐ it keeps Earth from getting too hot or cold.

Ⓑ it is made of gases, dust, and water.

Ⓒ it helps living things.

Ⓓ it is the same as on the other planets.

Earth (continued)

Read the following questions carefully. Use complete sentences to answer the questions. Possible answers below

6. What do scientists think Pluto is?

They think Pluto is an asteroid, a comet, or a small planet.

7. What shape is Earth?

Earth is round but a little pear-shaped.

8. What would happen to Earth if the sun were closer?

If the sun were closer, Earth would be too hot for life.

9. How does the magnetic field help Earth?

The magnetic field acts like a shield. It keeps dangerous radiation from the sun and space from reaching Earth.

10. What does Earth's surface look like from space?

Dark areas would be seas, and brown areas would be land.

Earth (continued)

Read the question below. Write complete sentences for your answer. Support your answer with information from the selection.

Linking to the Concepts What are the different ways that Earth is moving?

_____

_____

_____

_____

_____

Read the question below. Your answer should be based on your own experience. Write complete sentences for your answer.

Personal Response What is special about where you live on Earth?

_____

_____

_____

_____

_____

Earth (continued)

Grammar, Usage, and Mechanics

Read each question. Fill in the bubble beside the answer in each group that is correct. If none of the answers is correct, choose the last answer, "none of the above."

1. In which sentence do the subject and verb agree?

Ⓐ Several cows is walking across the field.

Ⓑ The windows shake when the wind blows.

Ⓒ A boy sit alone at the top of the stairs.

Ⓓ none of the above

2. In which sentence do the subject and verb agree?

Ⓐ The bag of bagels is new.   Ⓒ The mice is gray.

Ⓑ Many shoppers uses cards.   Ⓓ none of the above

3. In which sentence do the subject and verb agree?

Ⓐ The tree branches was old.   Ⓒ The cat sleep alone.

Ⓑ The scales on the fish is red. Ⓓ none of the above

4. In which sentence do the subject and verb *not* agree?

Ⓐ The workers spend a lot of time repairing roads.

Ⓑ Marty waters the plants on Tuesday and Saturday.

Ⓒ Each of the doors open automatically.

Ⓓ none of the above

5. In which sentence do the subject and verb *not* agree?

Ⓐ Most of the stores open at nine.

Ⓑ The lions sleeps under those trees.

Ⓒ This box weighs too much for us to carry.

Ⓓ none of the above

UNIT 4 **Lesson 5**

Earth (continued)

Analyzing the Selection

Read the questions below. Write complete sentences for your answer. Support your answer with information from the selection.

What are some things that have changed Earth's surface? Are all of them natural, or have people changed Earth? Include information from the selection, what you already know, and your opinion in your answer.

_____

_____

_____

_____

_____

_____

_____

_____

_____

_____

_____

_____

Earth (continued)

Oral Fluency Assessment

Nana's Birthday Gift

Grandmother's birthday was coming up. Kay decided to	1–8
make her a scrapbook as a gift. She wanted to show Nana all	9–21
the things they did together.	22–26
The scrapbook had to be special, just like Nana. She had	27–37
been a big part of Kay's life. When Kay was just a month old,	38–51
Nana started taking care of her. When Kay's parents went	52–61
to work, they drove Kay to Nana's house. The house felt	62–72
like home.	73–74
There were three main parts in the scrapbook. The first part	75–85
had pictures. There were lots of pictures. Kay loved the ones	86–96
that showed both of them at the park. The sandbox was their	97–108
best spot.	109–110
The next part was about the projects they made together.	111–120
Once they made a birdfeeder. Another time Nana taught Kay to	121–131
sew. Then there was the time they made a garden. They planted	132–143
tomatoes, carrots, and radishes. Nana and Kay still work on	144–153
the garden.	154–155
The last section was about their long trips together. Kay	156–165
put in some of their postcards. Kay hoped Nana would like the	166–176
scrapbook as much as Kay liked making it.	177–188

**EVALUATING CODES
FOR ORAL FLUENCY**

sky   (/) words read incorrectly

blue
  ^   sky   (^) inserted word
          ( ]) after the last word

READING RATE AND ACCURACY

Total Words Read: _____

Number of Errors: _____

Number of Correct Words
Read Per Minute (WPM):   _____

Accuracy Rate: _____

(Number of Correct Words Read per
Minute ÷ Total Words Read)

READING FLUENCY

	Low	Average	High
Decoding ability	○	○	○
Pace	○	○	○
Syntax	○	○	○
Self-correction	○	○	○
Intonation	○	○	○

Record student rates on the Oral Fluency Scores pages.

Name _____ **Date** _____ **Score** _____

Persuasive Writing

Writing Situation

Should people be exploring space

Audience

Your classmates

Directions for Writing

Some people think that we should not be exploring space. They say it is too dangerous and costs too much money. Present and support your opinion concerning space exploration.

Checklist

You will earn the best score if you

- think about your point of view before you start writing.
- state the issue and your point of view clearly in the first paragraph.
- include facts or examples that support your point of view.
- restate your point of view in the final paragraph.
- show that you care about the issue.
- write in a way that is interesting to your readers.
- write paragraphs that focus on related ideas.
- use transition words to go from one idea to another.
- write complete sentences and avoid fragments or run-ons.
- read your writing after you finish and check for mistakes.

Four Point Rubrics for Persuasive Writing

UNIT 4

Genre	1 Point	2 Points	3 Points	4 Points
Persuasive	Position is absent or confusing. Insufficient writing to show that criteria are met.	Position is vague or lacks clarity. Unrelated ideas or multiple positions are included.	An opening statement identifies position. Writing may develop few or more points than delineated in opening. Focus may be too broad.	Sets scope and purpose of paper in introduction. Maintains position throughout. Supports arguments. Includes effective closing.
Writing Traits				
Audience	Displays little or no sense of audience. Does not engage audience.	Displays some sense of audience.	Writes with audience in mind throughout.	Displays a strong sense of audience. Engages audience.
Focus	Topic is unclear or wanders and must be inferred. Extraneous material may be present.	Topic/position/direction is unclear and must be inferred.	Topic/position is stated and direction/purpose is previewed and maintained. Mainly stays on topic.	Topic/position is clearly stated, previewed, and maintained throughout the paper. Topics and details are tied together with a central theme or purpose that is maintained /threaded throughout the paper.
Organization	The writing lacks coherence; organization seems haphazard and disjointed. Plan is not evident. Facts are presented randomly. No transitions are included. Beginning is weak and ending is abrupt. There is no awareness of paragraph structure or organization.	An attempt has been made to organize the writing; however, the overall structure is inconsistent or skeletal. Plan is evident but loosely structured or writer overuses a particular pattern. Writing may be a listing of facts/ideas with a weak beginning or conclusion. Transitions are awkward or nonexistent. Includes beginning use of paragraphs.	Organization is clear and coherent. Order and structure are present, but may seem formulaic. Plan is evident. Reasons for order of key concepts may be unclear. Beginning or conclusion is included but may lack impact. Transitions are present. Paragraph use is appropriate.	The organization enhances the central idea and its development. The order and structure are compelling and move the reader through the text easily. Plan is evident. Key concepts are logically sequenced. Beginning grabs attention. Conclusion adds impact. Uses a variety of transitions that enhance meaning. Uses paragraphs appropriately.
Writing Conventions				
Conventions Overall	Numerous errors in usage, grammar, spelling, capitalization, and punctuation repeatedly distract the reader and make the text difficult to read. The reader finds it difficult to focus on the message.	The writing demonstrates limited control of standard writing conventions (punctuation, spelling, capitalization, grammar, and usage). Errors sometimes impede readability.	The writing demonstrates control of standard writing conventions (punctuation, spelling, capitalization, grammar, and usage). Minor errors, while perhaps noticeable, do not impede readability.	The writing demonstrates exceptionally strong control of standard writing conventions (punctuation, spelling, capitalization, grammar, and usage) and uses them effectively to enhance communication. Errors are so few and so minor that the reader can easily skim over them.

Name _____ Date _____ Score _____

The House on Maple Street

Vocabulary

Read each item. Fill in the bubble for the answer you think is correct.

1. What does the prefix *re-* mean?

- Ⓐ again
- Ⓒ before
- Ⓑ half
- Ⓓ not

2. If something is **sturdy,** it is

- Ⓐ old.
- Ⓒ short.
- Ⓑ dark.
- Ⓓ strong.

3. Ruby lost her cup in one of the **burrows. Burrows** are

- Ⓐ homes animals make high in the tops of trees.
- Ⓑ homes animals make on top of large rocks.
- Ⓒ homes animals make in holes in the ground.
- Ⓓ homes animals make in the bottom of streams.

4. The old farmhouse was **crumbling.** This means it was

- Ⓐ falling to pieces.
- Ⓒ still strong.
- Ⓑ being fixed.
- Ⓓ being used.

5. The stream slowed to a **trickle.** This means

- Ⓐ the stream moved along a new path.
- Ⓑ the water stopped running.
- Ⓒ it curved around a big bend of rock.
- Ⓓ only a small amount of water was left.

The House on Maple Street (continued)

Comprehension

Read the following questions carefully. Then completely fill in the bubble of each correct answer. You may look back at the selection to find the answer to each of the questions.

1. Which of these happened first?

Ⓐ People set up tepees near the stream.

Ⓑ Ruby played with her china dishes.

Ⓒ The woods caught fire.

Ⓓ The schoolteacher sold some of the land.

2. Who lost the arrowhead?

Ⓐ a great hunter

Ⓑ a young boy

Ⓒ the boy's friend

Ⓓ the father

The House on Maple Street (continued)

3. Ruby's father did all of these EXCEPT

    Ⓐ cutting down trees and building a house.

    Ⓑ pulling up the tree stumps left by the fire.

    Ⓒ plowing the land and planting crops.

    Ⓓ going with the wagon train to California.

4. Who first lived in the brick house on Maple Street?

    Ⓐ a man and woman with two girls named Chrissy and Jenny

    Ⓑ the young couple who built the house

    Ⓒ Ruby's father and his wife

    Ⓓ a schoolteacher and his family

5. Which of these is an opinion?

    Ⓐ Ruby's brother planted a row of trees along the road.

    Ⓑ Maple Street got better and better over the years.

    Ⓒ Maggie dug up a tiny china cup and an arrowhead.

    Ⓓ A man up the road filled in the stream.

The House on Maple Street (continued)

Read the following questions carefully. Use complete sentences to answer the questions. Possible answers below

6. What did Maple Street look like three hundred years ago?

There were no houses or a street; it was a forest with a bubbling brook.

7. Why did the tribes pack up and move away?

The tribes followed the buffalo so they would have food.

8. How did Ruby lose her cup and the arrowhead?

She left them outside, and a rabbit knocked them into his burrow.

9. Name the people who lived in the first house after Ruby grew up and moved away.

Ruby's brother and his family lived there.

10. What happened to the house Ruby lived in?

The house was torn down, and a red brick one was built on the spot.

The House on Maple Street (continued)

Read the question below. Write complete sentences for your answer. Support your answer with information from the selection.

Linking to the Concepts What parts of this selection could be real and what parts might be made up?

_____

_____

_____

_____

_____

Read the question below. Your answer should be based on your own experience. Write complete sentences for your answer.

Personal Response Many things change over time. What changes have you seen in your neighborhood since you started living in your home?

_____

_____

_____

_____

The House on Maple Street (continued)

Grammar, Usage, and Mechanics

Read each question. Fill in the bubble beside the answer in each group that is correct. If none of the answers is correct, choose the last answer, "none of the above."

1. In which sentence is the verb in the past tense?

Ⓐ Families visit this park. Ⓒ A tree fell loudly.

Ⓑ Flowers will grow here. Ⓓ none of the above

2. In which sentence is the verb in the future tense?

Ⓐ I will visit next week. Ⓒ Mom wants to sleep.

Ⓑ They came last year. Ⓓ none of the above

3. Which sentence uses the present perfect tense?

Ⓐ Many of the people in our area like sports.

Ⓑ The neighbors have joined a swim club.

Ⓒ We hope they invite us to swim with them.

Ⓓ none of the above

4. In which sentence is the verb tense correct?

Ⓐ Last week, it will be windy.

Ⓑ Dad mowed the lawn and pulls weeds.

Ⓒ The bread has finished in a few minutes.

Ⓓ none of the above

5. In which sentence is the verb tense correct?

Ⓐ Will's party was held at the skating rink last night.

Ⓑ My sister will meet us at the mall yesterday.

Ⓒ In a few days, Dad has returned from his trip.

Ⓓ none of the above

The House on Maple Street (continued)

Analyzing the Selection

Read the prompt below. Write complete sentences for your response.

In "The House on Maple Street," the spot where the house was built has changed over the years, but in many ways it has remained the same. Use information from the selection to describe some of the ways the spot has changed and ways it has remained the same.

_____

_____

_____

_____

_____

_____

_____

_____

_____

_____

_____

_____

_____

The House on Maple Street (continued)

Oral Fluency Assessment

Plants and You

If we did not have green plants, there would be no life on
Earth. There could be no fish, no birds, no animals, and no
people. All living creatures need plants.

Plants make their food from sunlight, air, and water. They
provide food for many other living things. Many animals eat
plants. Some creatures eat other creatures. However, all food
leads back to plants. This is called the "food chain."

People are at the top of the food chain. This is because we
eat many different things. The food chain ends with the animal
that will not be eaten by other animals for food.

Besides providing food, plants are vital because they make
the oxygen that we breathe. Plants take in the air that we
breathe out. Then they change it to oxygen. All animals depend
on oxygen.

Besides food and air, plants give us wood to build our
homes. They help keep us cool with their shade. Plants give us
medicine. Plants are pretty to look at, too. Life would not be
good at all if we did not have plants.

1–13
14–25
26–31
32–41
42–51
52–60
61–70
71–83
84–94
95–104
105–113
114–125
126–136
137–138
139–149
150–161
162–173
174–182

**EVALUATING CODES
FOR ORAL FLUENCY**

sky   (/) words read incorrectly

blue
  ^ sky   (^) inserted word
          ( ]) after the last word

READING RATE AND ACCURACY

Total Words Read: _____

Number of Errors: _____

Number of Correct Words
Read Per Minute (WPM):   _____

Accuracy Rate: _____

(Number of Correct Words Read per
Minute ÷ Total Words Read)

READING FLUENCY

	Low	Average	High
Decoding ability	○	○	○
Pace	○	○	○
Syntax	○	○	○
Self-correction	○	○	○
Intonation	○	○	○

Record student rate on the Oral Fluency Score pages.

Name _____ Date _____ Score _____

Days of Digging

Vocabulary

Read each item. Fill in the bubble for the answer you think is correct.

1. Which prefix means "not"?

Ⓐ *bi-*   Ⓒ *auto-*

Ⓑ *dis-*   Ⓓ *mid-*

2. A culture's **origins** are its

Ⓐ feelings.   Ⓒ problems.

Ⓑ thoughts.   Ⓓ beginnings.

3. A **laboratory** is a place to

Ⓐ do experiments and tests.

Ⓑ store artifacts and discoveries.

Ⓒ put extra dirt and rocks.

Ⓓ keep food for the team.

4. Every inch of the dig was **charted.** This means the team

Ⓐ dug up the whole area.

Ⓑ took pictures of everything.

Ⓒ brushed each piece carefully.

Ⓓ mapped the whole area.

5. An archaeologist may study a **ruin** of a city. A **ruin**

Ⓐ looks like it did long ago.

Ⓑ has just been built.

Ⓒ is damaged or destroyed.

Ⓓ was built underground.

Days of Digging (continued)

Comprehension

Read the following questions carefully. Then completely fill in the bubble of each correct answer. You may look back at the selection to find the answer to each of the questions.

1. Why did the archaeologists boil water?

Ⓐ to make tea or coffee

Ⓑ to clean off the artifacts

Ⓒ to make it safe to drink

Ⓓ to keep themselves warm

2. What is a field book used for?

Ⓐ to look up important facts

Ⓑ to keep notes about the dig

Ⓒ to study pictures of objects

Ⓓ to keep a record of money

Days of Digging (continued)

3. How do archaeologists work on a dig?

    Ⓐ as quickly as they can

    Ⓑ in many different spots at one time

    Ⓒ all alone

    Ⓓ slowly and carefully

4. Archaeology is the science of

    Ⓐ finding and studying past cultures.

    Ⓑ digging up and studying dinosaurs.

    Ⓒ studying rocks and layers of earth.

    Ⓓ digging up rocks and minerals.

5. Archaeologists do all of these EXCEPT

    Ⓐ study a culture and its origins.

    Ⓑ solve mysteries about a culture.

    Ⓒ break artifacts apart to study them.

    Ⓓ find out why cultures did certain things.

Days of Digging (continued)

Read the following questions carefully. Use complete sentences to answer the questions. Possible answers below

6. Why is every inch of the dig mapped?

Mapping helps archaeologists track where each artifact was found.

7. What happens to artifacts after they are drawn, numbered, and photographed?

They are examined, and then they are packed and sent to a museum.

8. What did the team in the selection find first?

They found bones with possible human scratches and marks.

9. Why did the author write the selection using the word "you" as if the reader were part of the story?

The author wanted to make readers feel as if they were part of the dig.

10. Why is it important to learn about our human past?

It teaches us about other cultures and how we became what we are today.

Days of Digging (continued)

Read the question below. Write complete sentences for your answer. Support your answer with information from the selection.

Linking to the Concepts Why is being an archaeologist a difficult, but exciting, job?

_____

_____

_____

_____

Read the question below. Your answer should be based on your own experience. Write complete sentences for your answer.

Personal Response Where in the world would you like to be involved in an archaeological dig and what would you hope to find there?

_____

_____

_____

_____

Days of Digging (continued)

Grammar, Usage, and Mechanics

Read each question. Fill in the bubble beside the answer in each group that is correct. If none of the answers is correct, choose the last answer, "none of the above."

1. Which item is a preposition?

Ⓐ the   Ⓒ new

Ⓑ in   Ⓓ none of the above

2. In which sentence is a prepositional phrase underlined?

Ⓐ Buy a piece <u>of wood</u>.   Ⓒ Buy <u>a piece</u> of wood.

Ⓑ <u>Buy a</u> piece of wood.   Ⓓ none of the above

3. In which sentence is a prepositional phrase underlined?

Ⓐ The <u>store on</u> the corner sells bicycles and skis.

Ⓑ The store on the corner sells bicycles <u>and skis</u>.

Ⓒ The store on the <u>corner sells</u> bicycles and skis.

Ⓓ none of the above

4. Which shows the object of the preposition underlined?

Ⓐ Maddie walked <u>carefully</u> into the water.

Ⓑ Maddie <u>walked</u> carefully into the water.

Ⓒ Maddie walked carefully into the <u>water</u>.

Ⓓ none of the above

5. Which underlined word is modified by a prepositional phrase?

Ⓐ The <u>picture</u> on the wall was taken long ago.

Ⓑ The picture on the wall was taken <u>long</u> ago.

Ⓒ The picture on the <u>wall</u> was taken long ago.

Ⓓ none of the above

Days of Digging (continued)

Analyzing the Selection

Read the questions below. Write complete sentences for your answer. Support your answer with information from the selection.

Imagine that you are part of an archaeological dig. What role would you like to play, and why would you choose this role? What are some of the things you would do as part of the team?

_____

_____

_____

_____

_____

_____

_____

_____

_____

_____

Days of Digging (continued)

Oral Fluency Assessment

Our National Bird

The bald eagle is one of the largest birds in America. It is	1–13
a beautiful bird. However, it is not bald. An eagle has white	14–25
feathers on its head. The eagle's name comes from an old word.	26–37
The word is *piebald*. It means "marked with white."	38–46
Most people do not know that eagles like to eat fish. This is	47–59
why they live near water. You can spot them at rivers, lakes,	60–71
and the ocean.	72–74
Bald eagles are rare. They are found only in America. That is	75–86
one reason why we made the bald eagle our national bird.	87–97
Many people like the eagle as a symbol for our country.	98–108
They like what the eagle stands for. It represents freedom and	109–119
strength for them.	120–122
Ben Franklin was not one of these people. He was not a fan	123–135
of the bald eagle. He once wrote a letter to his daughter. In it,	136–149
he said eagles robbed other birds. He also said eagles were not	150–161
brave. They flew away when small birds came after them. He	162–172
wanted the turkey to be the national bird.	173–180

EVALUATING CODES FOR ORAL FLUENCY

sky (/) words read incorrectly

blue
^ sky (^) inserted word
( ]) after the last word

READING RATE AND ACCURACY

Total Words Read: _____

Number of Errors: _____

Number of Correct Words Read Per Minute (WPM): _____

Accuracy Rate: _____

(Number of Correct Words Read per Minute ÷ Total Words Read)

READING FLUENCY

	Low	Average	High
Decoding ability	○	○	○
Pace	○	○	○
Syntax	○	○	○
Self-correction	○	○	○
Intonation	○	○	○

Record student rates on the Oral Fluency Scores pages.

Name _____ Date _____ Score _____

Earthquake! The 1906 San Francisco Nightmare

Vocabulary

Read each item. Fill in the bubble for the answer you think is correct.

1. A **section** is a(n)

- Ⓐ army.
- Ⓑ city.
- Ⓒ plan.
- Ⓓ piece.

2. The inflectional ending **-ed** tells you an action

- Ⓐ can not happen.
- Ⓑ is happening now.
- Ⓒ happened in the past.
- Ⓓ will happen in the future.

3. There is often a **rumble** during a quake. A **rumble** is

- Ⓐ a heavy, deep, rolling sound.
- Ⓑ a wild and scary shaking of earth.
- Ⓒ a dark puff of smoke.
- Ⓓ a quiet moment.

4. **Shattered** windows lay on the ground. **Shattered** means the windows

- Ⓐ had many different panes.
- Ⓑ were broken into tiny pieces.
- Ⓒ were made from colored glass.
- Ⓓ had been painted shut.

5. When something is **tough,** it is

- Ⓐ original.
- Ⓑ easy to do.
- Ⓒ missing.
- Ⓓ difficult to do.

UNIT 5 Lesson 3

Earthquake! The 1906 San Francisco Nightmare (continued)

Comprehension

Read the following questions carefully. Then completely fill in the bubble of each correct answer. You may look back at the selection to find the answer to each of the questions.

1. Why could firefighters not put out the San Francisco fire?

　Ⓐ The pipes had burst, so there was no water.

　Ⓑ They could not get to fires on the broken streets.

　Ⓒ It was too dangerous because of the flying stones.

　Ⓓ Gas fires cannot be put out with water.

2. To stop the fire from spreading, soldiers

　Ⓐ beat the fire with coats and brooms.

　Ⓑ sprayed the flames with hoses.

　Ⓒ blew up buildings.

　Ⓓ rode horses to get close to the flames.

Earthquake! The 1906 San Francisco Nightmare (continued)

3. All of these are true about earthquakes EXCEPT

  Ⓐ shock waves occur when tectonic plates slip while they are pushing.

  Ⓑ the waves start below Earth's surface and move up through the ground.

  Ⓒ hot liquid rock pushing up under Earth's surface makes waves.

  Ⓓ earthquakes usually happen along faults, weak places in the crust.

4. Where was America's strongest earthquake?

  Ⓐ Fort Tejon, California

  Ⓑ Rat Islands, Alaska

  Ⓒ New Madrid, Missouri

  Ⓓ Prince William Sound, Alaska

5. Which of these is an opinion about the San Francisco earthquake?

  Ⓐ Thousands of people camped in tents afterwards.

  Ⓑ It was America's most harmful earthquake.

  Ⓒ About 225,000 people were hurt.

  Ⓓ It took millions of dollars to rebuild the city.

Earthquake! The 1906 San Francisco Nightmare (continued)

Read the following questions carefully. Use complete sentences to answer the questions. Possible answers below

6. What causes the noise during an earthquake?

The noise is the sound of the ground moving and the buildings being shaken.

7. What causes aftershocks?

Aftershocks happen when the tectonic plates move into their new positions.

8. Why was the San Francisco earthquake so harmful?

It hit a big city with many buildings and people, and the city was unprepared.

9. What changes did San Francisco make after the earthquake?

They did not build on soft earth, and used steel frames and bendable pipes.

10. According to the selection, how are earthquakes measured?

They use a seismograph to record movement. The Richter Scale tells how powerful it is.

Earthquake! The 1906 San Francisco Nightmare (continued)

Read the question below. Write complete sentences for your answer. Support your answer with information from the selection.

Linking to the Concepts When earthquakes happen in the future, how will we be better prepared?

_____

_____

_____

_____

_____

Read the question below. Your answer should be based on your own experience. Write complete sentences for your answer.

Personal Response How would camping out after the San Francisco earthquake be different from camping out for fun?

_____

_____

_____

_____

_____

Earthquake! The 1906 San Francisco Nightmare (continued)

Grammar, Usage, and Mechanics

Read each question. Fill in the bubble beside the answer in each group that is correct. If none of the answers is correct, choose the last answer, "none of the above."

1. Which of these verbs is in the past tense?

Ⓐ is climbing   Ⓒ wrapped

Ⓑ will stand   Ⓓ none of the above

2. Which of these verbs is in the future tense?

Ⓐ has reached   Ⓒ were hiking

Ⓑ will build   Ⓓ none of the above

3. Which verb is in the present tense?

Ⓐ catch

Ⓑ opened

Ⓒ will burn

Ⓓ none of the above

4. Which sentence is in the past tense?

Ⓐ The ship sailed into the distance.

Ⓑ The plane will land shortly.

Ⓒ Trains stop here every hour.

Ⓓ none of the above

5. Which sentence is in the future tense?

Ⓐ My sister called to say she would be late.

Ⓑ My sister will call in a few minutes.

Ⓒ My sister calls often.

Ⓓ none of the above

Earthquake! The 1906 San Francisco Nightmare (continued)

Analyzing the Selection

Read the question below. Write complete sentences for your answer. Support your answer with information from the selections.

In the selections "The House on Maple Street" and "Earthquake!" changes happened to an area. How were the changes similar, and how were they different? Consider things like the size of the area, the population, the type of changes, the speed of changes, and other ideas of your own.

_____

_____

_____

_____

_____

_____

_____

_____

_____

_____

_____

Earthquake! The 1906 San Francisco Nightmare (continued)

Oral Fluency Assessment

A Night in a Camper

Paul was excited. He was going camping with his Aunt Eve
and Uncle Bart. He had never gone camping before and was
not sure what to bring. He decided he needed his sleeping bag,
backpack, hiking shoes, and a few other things.

On Friday morning, Paul's mother woke him up early. He got
ready and sat on the porch waiting. Soon he saw a big camper
pull up to his house. He did not know what to think. Then his
father brought him to the camper and opened the door. Aunt
Eve and Uncle Bart were inside; this was their camper.

A few hours later, the three of them arrived at their site. It
was a campground in the mountains. They found a spot and
pulled in. Then they all went hiking. When they returned to the
camper, they had a nice meal that Uncle Bart had cooked on a
small stove. When it was time to go to sleep, Paul had his own
bed. He was having a fabulous time.

Line
1–11
12–22
23–34
35–42
43–53
54–66
67–80
81–91
92–101
102–114
115–125
126–137
138–150
151–164
165–171

EVALUATING CODES FOR ORAL FLUENCY

sky   (/) words read incorrectly

blue
^ sky   (^) inserted word
        ( ]) after the last word

READING RATE AND ACCURACY

Total Words Read: _____

Number of Errors: _____

Number of Correct Words
Read Per Minute (WPM): _____

Accuracy Rate: _____

(Number of Correct Words Read per
Minute ÷ Total Words Read)

READING FLUENCY

	Low	Average	High
Decoding ability	○	○	○
Pace	○	○	○
Syntax	○	○	○
Self-correction	○	○	○
Intonation	○	○	○

Record student rates on the Oral Fluency Scores pages.

Name _____ Date _____ Score _____

The Disappearing Island

Vocabulary

Read each item. Fill in the bubble for the answer you think is correct.

1. Which word belongs in this base word family?

_____, **unimaginative, imagination**

Ⓐ planned   Ⓒ thought

Ⓑ considered   Ⓓ imagined

2. Toppled means made something

Ⓐ sail.   Ⓒ fall.

Ⓑ run.   Ⓓ spin.

3. The sea will **claim** things on the beach. This means it will

Ⓐ make thing like new.   Ⓒ leave things alone.

Ⓑ tip things over.   Ⓓ take things for its own.

4. The waves left **ripples** in the sand. **Ripples** are a type of

Ⓐ design.   Ⓒ shell.

Ⓑ rock.   Ⓓ flower.

5. The island had **acres** of tidal pools. An **acre** is

Ⓐ a small group.

Ⓑ a measure of area.

Ⓒ an area covered with water.

Ⓓ a hidden body of water.

UNIT 5 Lesson 4

The Disappearing Island (continued)

Comprehension

Read the following questions carefully. Then completely fill in the bubble of each correct answer. You may look back at the selection to find the answer to each of the questions.

1. Carrie got all of these for her birthday EXCEPT

Ⓐ a cake.

Ⓑ a perfect sand dollar.

Ⓒ a new life jacket.

Ⓓ a trip to a disappearing island.

2. How did Carrie see the island from the boat?

Ⓐ by looking behind the boat

Ⓑ by looking through binoculars

Ⓒ by watching a cormorant land

Ⓓ by wading close to shore

The Disappearing Island (continued)

3. What did Carrie find in the sand?

Ⓐ a broken brick

Ⓑ a pretty shell

Ⓒ a sand dollar

Ⓓ a whale backbone

4. What did Carrie imagine?

Ⓐ that everything was swimming and orange

Ⓑ that the breakwater would last forever

Ⓒ that she was a grandmother coming to the island

Ⓓ that she visited the lighthouse keeper's daughter

5. The author's main purpose in writing this selection was to

Ⓐ explain how the ocean changes an island over time.

Ⓑ persuade people to enjoy life more.

Ⓒ show how to explore a beach.

Ⓓ make the readers feel as if they are walking up the lighthouse.

The Disappearing Island (continued)

Read the following questions carefully. Use complete sentences to answer the questions. Possible answers below

6. How was high tide different from low tide in Wellfleet Harbor?

At high tide the water was much deeper; it was way over Carrie's head.

7. What did the island look like when Carrie saw it?

It had sand, shells, and mussels covering the stones in the tidal pools.

8. Why had the island changed from a century before?

The ocean started eroding the island, so people moved away.

9. What happened to the lighthouses?

The first toppled into the sea. The second was knocked down by the sea.

10. What was the breakwater and why was it built?

It was a rock barrier made to protect the island and the lighthouse from the sea.

The Disappearing Island (continued)

Read the question below. Write complete sentences for your answer. Support your answer with information from the selection.

Linking to the Concepts Why is a tide chart important in this selection?

_____

_____

_____

_____

_____

Read the questions below. Your answer should be based on your own experience. Write complete sentences for your answer.

Personal Response What do you think Carrie will remember most about her ninth birthday? Why do you think that?

_____

_____

_____

_____

_____

The Disappearing Island (continued)

Grammar, Usage, and Mechanics

Read each question. Fill in the bubble beside the answer in each group that is correct. If none of the answers is correct, choose the last answer, "none of the above."

1. In which sentence is the verb correct?

Ⓐ The game are at Elm.   Ⓒ The game were at Elm.

🅑 The game was at Elm.   Ⓓ none of the above

2. In which sentence is the verb correct?

🅐 Joe is a good golfer.   Ⓒ Joe are a good golfer.

Ⓑ Joe am a good golfer.   Ⓓ none of the above

3. In which sentence is the verb correct?

Ⓐ Bob knowed the way to the lake.

Ⓑ Nora drawed a picture of her dog.

Ⓒ The pond freezed last night.

🅓 none of the above

4. In which sentence is the verb correct?

Ⓐ Everybody lefted around four o'clock.

Ⓑ Three of us rided our bikes to school.

🅒 The mail carrier gave us a package.

Ⓓ none of the above

5. In which sentence is the verb correct?

Ⓐ Lynn hanged the feeder on the tree.

🅑 Jim brought salad to the picnic.

Ⓒ My brother tored his shirt.

Ⓓ none of the above

The Disappearing Island • **Lesson Assessment Book 2**

The Disappearing Island (continued)

Analyzing the Selection

Read the question below. Write complete sentences for your answer. Support your answer with information from the selection.

Imagine that you were part of this birthday adventure. Which parts would you have liked best, and why would these parts be so important to you?

_____

_____

_____

_____

_____

_____

_____

_____

_____

_____

_____

_____

The Disappearing Island (continued)

Oral Fluency Assessment

A New King

All the monkeys in the forest were excited. This was the day	1–12
the new leader of the monkeys would be picked.	13–21
By noon, all of the monkeys had gathered near a sacred tree.	22–33
The old King of the Monkeys was named Butu. He would help	34–45
to choose the new king.	46–50
Many monkeys wanted to be king. They climbed up and	51–60
down the sacred tree quickly. The monkey that did the best	61–71
tricks would be the new king.	72–77
One monkey climbed and jumped better than all the others.	78–87
Butu decided this monkey would be king. When the monkey	88–97
climbed to the top of the tree to receive the crown, everyone	98–109
was surprised. This monkey was a girl! Girls could not be king!	110–121
Butu thought very hard. Chota was the best climber and	122–131
jumper. Yet she was a girl. Then Butu had an idea. He said,	132–144
"Chota is the best climber and jumper, but she can not be king.	145–157
So this year, we will have a queen instead." He gave Chota the	158–170
crown. All the monkeys cheered.	171–175

EVALUATING CODES FOR ORAL FLUENCY

sky	(/) words read incorrectly
blue	
^ sky	(^) inserted word
	( ]) after the last word

READING RATE AND ACCURACY

Total Words Read: _____

Number of Errors: _____

Number of Correct Words
Read Per Minute (WPM): _____

Accuracy Rate: _____

(Number of Correct Words Read per
Minute ÷ Total Words Read)

READING FLUENCY

	Low	Average	High
Decoding ability	○	○	○
Pace	○	○	○
Syntax	○	○	○
Self-correction	○	○	○
Intonation	○	○	○

Record student rates on the Oral Fluency Scores pages.

Name _____ Date _____ Score _____

What Ever Happened to the Baxter Place?

Vocabulary

Read each item. Fill in the bubble for the answer you think is correct.

1. What does the prefix **un-** mean?

   Ⓐ again

   Ⓑ before

   Ⓒ under

   Ⓓ not

2. **Necessities** are

   Ⓐ needed things

   Ⓑ extra things.

   Ⓒ new things.

   Ⓓ borrowed things.

3. The farmers had **installed** milking parlors. In this sentence, **installed** means

   Ⓐ invented.

   Ⓑ fixed.

   Ⓒ put into place.

   Ⓓ closed.

4. A **particular** piece of land is

   Ⓐ beside a pond.

   Ⓑ covered with trees.

   Ⓒ special in some way.

   Ⓓ difficult to farm.

5. Many crops are **seasonal.** This means the crops

   Ⓐ can grow even in winter.

   Ⓑ are ripe at a certain time.

   Ⓒ must be picked by hand.

   Ⓓ cost more than other crops.

What Ever Happened to the Baxter Place? (continued)

Comprehension

Read the following questions carefully. Then completely fill in the bubble of each correct answer. You may look back at the selection to find the answer to each of the questions.

1. From what point of view is this selection written?

  Ⓐ in the first-person by a Baxter

  Ⓑ in the first-person by a visitor

  Ⓒ in the third-person by an outside observer

  Ⓓ in the third-person by someone in the selection

2. This selection is mostly about

  Ⓐ a farm that gradually changes over time.

  Ⓑ a new shopping mall.

  Ⓒ why farming is such a hard life.

  Ⓓ how money can change people.

What Ever Happened to the Baxter Place? (continued)

3. What was the Baxter Place like at the beginning of the selection?

Ⓐ a field with lakes and streams

Ⓑ a forest full of trees

Ⓒ a small town with just a few houses

Ⓓ a big, old-fashioned farm

4. From the selection, you know that the Baxter Place

Ⓐ produced good crops.

Ⓑ was very pretty.

Ⓒ had poor soil.

Ⓓ was hard to find.

5. The effect of all the changes to the Baxter Place is that it is

Ⓐ bigger than it ever was.

Ⓑ owned by Homestead Realty.

Ⓒ half its original size.

Ⓓ part of a shopping mall.

What Ever Happened to the Baxter Place? (continued)

Read the following questions carefully. Use complete sentences to answer the questions. Possible answers below

6. At the end of the selection, people could not say what happened to the Baxter Place. Why not?

The farm became smaller and changed slowly over a long period of time.

7. What was the first change to the Baxter Place?

Sara and Pete sold some land to Jess Hammil, who opened a market.

8. What happened when Sara asked Homestead Realty to save some of the trees when they built the new houses?

Price told her they would do their best, but only a few trees were left.

9. Why did the Homestead Realty Company build houses rather than keep the land for farming?

Their business is housing; the land was worth more for houses.

10. What did George Stillwell do with the land after he bought it from the Baxters?

He turned it into a motor lodge and tennis club.

What Ever Happened to the Baxter Place? (continued)

Read the question below. Write complete sentences for your answer. Support your answer with information from the selection.

Linking to the Concepts Why did the Baxter family sell so much of their farmland?

_____

_____

_____

_____

_____

_____

Read the question below. Your answer should be based on your own experience. Write complete sentences for your answer.

Personal Response Do you think the Baxters were sorry after they sold all their land? Explain your answer.

_____

_____

_____

_____

_____

What Ever Happened to the Baxter Place? (continued)

Grammar, Usage, and Mechanics

Read each question. Fill in the bubble beside the answer in each group that is correct. If none of the answers is correct, choose the last answer, "none of the above."

1. Which of these is a complex sentence?

Ⓐ The mop is new.   Ⓒ As I ate, Mom talked.

Ⓑ Ruth fixed the flat.   Ⓓ none of the above

2. Which of these is a complex sentence?

Ⓐ Ducks and geese landed.

Ⓑ They made a fire and cooked.

Ⓒ It is too big for that pot.

Ⓓ none of the above

3. The crowd roared when Roxie scored a goal. What is the independent clause in this sentence?

Ⓐ The crowd roared   Ⓒ roared when

Ⓑ when Roxie scored   Ⓓ none of the above

4. After Lou finished lunch, he walked to the library. What is the dependent clause in this sentence?

Ⓐ he walked to the library   Ⓒ he walked

Ⓑ After Lou finished lunch   Ⓓ none of the above

5. The car stopped. Children crossed the street. What is the best way to combine these two sentences?

Ⓐ The car stopped and crossed the street.

Ⓑ The car stopped while children crossed the street.

Ⓒ The car stopped the children crossing the street.

Ⓓ none of the above

What Ever Happened to the Baxter Place? (continued)

Analyzing the Selection

Read the questions below. Write complete sentences for your answer. Support your answer with information from the selections.

Some of the selections in this unit talked about how places have changed over time. These changes have both good and bad results. Are changes happening in your area? Do you think they are good or bad?

_____

_____

_____

_____

_____

_____

_____

_____

_____

_____

_____

_____

_____

What Ever Happened to the Baxter Place? (continued)

Oral Fluency Assessment

Comets and Snowballs

Have you ever looked long and hard at a snowball? If you	1–12
did, you might see that a snowball is not made of pure snow. A	13–26
snowball might have leaves, dirt, or even stones in it. And if it is	27–40
not packed tightly, there can be air inside as well.	41–50
You have probably heard of comets. Comets fly through our	51–60
solar system. They are like tiny planets that go around the sun.	61–72
And comets are a lot like dirty snowballs! Why? Comets are	73–83
made of dust and rock and ice. Just like snowballs, comets can	84–95
have pockets of air or gas inside of them.	96–104
Imagine that you could throw a snowball the length of a	105–115
football field. As the snowball flew, parts of it might fly off.	116–127
Comets are like snowballs in that way, too. As they fly through	128–139
space, comets can have a bright "tail." This tail seems to be	140–151
made of bits of the comet that "burn" off due to the sun's heat.	152–165
Think about this the next time that you see a starry	166–176
sky. Imagine all of the dirty snowballs out there, flying	177–186
through space!	187–188

EVALUATING CODES FOR ORAL FLUENCY

sky   (/) words read incorrectly

blue
 ^   sky   (^) inserted word
          ( ]) after the last word

READING RATE AND ACCURACY

Total Words Read: _____

Number of Errors: _____

Number of Correct Words
Read Per Minute (WPM): _____

Accuracy Rate: _____

(Number of Correct Words Read per
Minute ÷ Total Words Read)

READING FLUENCY

	Low	Average	High
Decoding ability	○	○	○
Pace	○	○	○
Syntax	○	○	○
Self-correction	○	○	○
Intonation	○	○	○

Record student rates on the Oral Fluency Scores pages.

Name _____ **Date** _____ **Score** _____

Expository Writing

Writing Situation
Changes that have happened in the area in which you live

Audience
People who live in another place

Directions for Writing
Write about how the place in which you live is changing. It can be any type of change, from a new building to something natural, such as minor flooding. Describe the change using enough details so the reader can visualize what has happened.

Checklist
You will earn the best score if you
- think about the change in your area before you start writing.
- describe the change in the first paragraph.
- use describing words so the reader can visualize the change.
- write paragraphs that focus on related ideas.
- use transition words to go from one idea to another.
- vary your sentences and the words you use.
- tell about the place where the change took place.
- give many interesting details.
- use subjects, verbs, and modifiers correctly.
- use comparison words so the reader will understand the change.

Four Point Rubrics for Expository Writing

Genre	1 Point	2 Points	3 Points	4 Points
Expository	Composition has no introduction or clear topic. It offers a group of loosely related facts or a series of poorly written steps. No conclusion is included.	Composition is clearly organized around main points with supportive facts or assertions. Composition has no clear introduction, but its topic is identifiable. However, it includes many facts unrelated to the topic, or it describes things in a disorganized way. No conclusion is included.	Main points and supportive details can be identified, but they are not clearly marked. Composition has an introduction and offers facts about the topic. Some facts may be irrelevant, or some ideas may be vague or out of order. The report is fairly well organized but doesn't have a strong conclusion.	Traces and constructs a line of argument, identifying part-to-whole relations. Main points are supported with logical and appropriate evidence. Composition begins with an introduction and offers relevant facts about the topic or describes the topic appropriately. The report is organized using cause/effect, comparison/contrast, or another pattern. It ends with a strong conclusion.
Writing Traits				
Focus	Topic is unclear or wanders and must be inferred. Extraneous material may be present.	Topic/position/direction is unclear and must be inferred.	Topic/position is stated and maintained. Mainly stays on topic.	Topic/position is clearly stated, previewed, and maintained throughout the paper. Topics and details are tied together with a central theme or purpose that is maintained /threaded throughout the paper.
Ideas/Content	Superficial and/or minimal content is included.	Main ideas are understandable, although they may be overly broad or simplistic, and the results may not be effective. Supporting detail is limited, insubstantial, overly general or off topic.	The writing is clear and focused. The reader can easily understand the main ideas. Support is present, although it may be limited or rather general.	Writing is exceptionally clear, focused, and interesting. Main ideas stand out and are developed by strong support and rich details.
Elaboration (supporting details and examples that develop the main idea)	States ideas or points with minimal detail to support them.	Includes sketchy, redundant, or general details; some may be irrelevant. Support for key ideas is very uneven.	Includes mix of general statements and specific details/examples. Support is mostly relevant but may be uneven and lack depth in places.	Includes specific details and supporting examples for each key point/idea. May use compare/contrast to support.
Writing Conventions				
Conventions Overall	Numerous errors in usage, grammar, spelling, capitalization, and punctuation repeatedly distract the reader and make the text difficult to read. The reader finds it difficult to focus on the message.	The writing demonstrates limited control of standard writing conventions (punctuation, spelling, capitalization, grammar, and usage). Errors sometimes impede readability.	The writing demonstrates control of standard writing conventions (punctuation, spelling, capitalization, grammar, and usage). Minor errors, while perhaps noticeable, do not impede readability.	The writing demonstrates exceptionally strong control of standard writing conventions (punctuation, spelling, capitalization, grammar, and usage) and uses them effectively to enhance communication. Errors are so few and so minor that the reader can easily skim over them.

Name _____ Date _____ Score _____

Tomás and the Library Lady

Vocabulary

Read each item. Fill in the bubble for the answer you think is correct.

1. A **cot** is a

   Ⓐ tasty fruit.   Ⓒ small bed.

   Ⓑ book.   Ⓓ toy.

2. A antonym for **setting** is

   Ⓐ hot.   Ⓒ bright.

   Ⓑ cloudy.   Ⓓ rising.

3. Tomás liked to **borrow** books from the library. To **borrow** books is to

   Ⓐ keep them for yourself.

   Ⓑ use and return them.

   Ⓒ read them quickly.

   Ⓓ sell them for a profit.

4. Tomás was **eager** to read. **Eager** means to

   Ⓐ want something very much.

   Ⓑ have little interest in something.

   Ⓒ not understand something.

   Ⓓ try very hard but fail.

5. Tomás saw dinosaurs **lap** water. In this sentence, **lap** means

   Ⓐ take a bath in.   Ⓒ walk through.

   Ⓑ lick up.   Ⓓ splash in.

Tomás and the Library Lady (continued)

Comprehension

Read the following questions carefully. Then completely fill in the bubble of each correct answer. You may look back at the selection to find the answer to each of the questions.

1. Why did Tomás go to Iowa?

   Ⓐ His family went to pick crops.

   Ⓑ He was visiting his grandfather.

   Ⓒ He wanted to see a new place.

   Ⓓ His family was going on vacation.

2. When Tomás first got to the library, he felt

   Ⓐ excited.

   Ⓑ scared.

   Ⓒ happy.

   Ⓓ sad.

Tomás and the Library Lady (continued)

3. What happened to Tomás when he read books?

   Ⓐ He wished his family went to the library.

   Ⓑ He wanted to go back to Texas.

   Ⓒ He could not read English words.

   Ⓓ He put himself in the stories.

4. Why did the author write this selection?

   Ⓐ to show why a family moved

   Ⓑ to explain about dinosaurs

   Ⓒ to tell a story about a boy enjoying a library

   Ⓓ to help readers learn some new Spanish words

5. What present did the library lady give Tomás when he left?

   Ⓐ a shiny new book

   Ⓑ *pan dulce*

   Ⓒ an old library book

   Ⓓ a ball for Enrique

Tomás and the Library Lady (continued)

Read the following questions carefully. Use complete sentences to answer the questions. Possible answers below

6. Why did Papá Grande tell Tomás to go to the library?

Papá Grande wanted Tomás to find new stories to teach the family.

7. How did Tomás's visits to the library help his family?

Tomás read the books to his family, so they all learned new stories.

8. What did Tomás's parents look for at the town dump?

Tomás's parents looked for pieces of iron to sell.

9. How did Tomás and the library lady help each other?

The library lady found books for Tomás, and he taught her words in Spanish.

10. Why did Tomás teach the library lady a sad word?

Tomás was going back to Texas, and he would miss her, the library, and the books.

Tomás and the Library Lady (continued)

Read the question below. Write complete sentences for your answer. Support your answer with information from the selection.

Linking to the Concepts How do you think Tomás's life will be different now that he has visited the library?

_____

_____

_____

_____

_____

Read the question below. Your answer should be based on your own experience. Write complete sentences for your answer.

Personal Response Write about a time when you imagined yourself in a story. What story was it, and how did you fit into that story?

_____

_____

_____

_____

_____

Tomás and the Library Lady (continued)

Grammar, Usage, and Mechanics

Read each question. Fill in the bubble beside the answer in each group that is correct. If none of the answers is correct, choose the last answer, "none of the above."

1. In which sentence is a noun underlined?

Ⓐ The big waves <u>crashed</u>.   Ⓒ The <u>big</u> waves crashed.

Ⓑ The big <u>waves</u> crashed.   Ⓓ none of the above

2. In which simple sentence is a verb underlined?

Ⓐ The flashlight needed new <u>batteries</u>.

Ⓑ The <u>flashlight</u> needed new batteries.

Ⓒ The flashlight needed <u>new</u> batteries.

Ⓓ none of the above

3. In which sentence is a proper noun underlined?

Ⓐ Some mountains in <u>Europe</u> have snow all year.

Ⓑ Some mountains in Europe have <u>snow</u> all year.

Ⓒ Some <u>mountains</u> in Europe have snow all year.

Ⓓ none of the above

4. In which sentence is a state-of-being verb underlined?

Ⓐ The baby <u>cries</u>.   Ⓒ The leaves <u>were</u> old.

Ⓑ Some dogs <u>played</u>.   Ⓓ none of the above

5. Which sentence has a compound subject?

Ⓐ Grass and weeds grew in the empty lot.

Ⓑ The city tore down and replaced the building.

Ⓒ A new school will be built there.

Ⓓ none of the above

Tomás and the Library Lady (continued)

Analyzing the Selection

Read the questions below. Write complete sentences for your answer. Support your answer with information from the selection.

Why do you think the library was so important to Tomás? Why was the library lady so willing to help him?

_____

_____

_____

_____

_____

_____

_____

_____

_____

_____

_____

_____

_____

Tomás and the Library Lady (continued)

Oral Fluency Assessment

The Plant Explorer

In today's world, most people have safe jobs. Things were not always that way. It used to be very different. Much about the world was not known. Even a job as a gardener might lead to big adventure.

Frank Meyer was born in 1875. He was interested in plants at a young age. No one was surprised when Frank became a "plant explorer." Frank's job was to go around the world. He found and collected plants.

Frank went back and forth from China. He went to other places in Asia, too. For fifteen years, Frank explored. He even had to escape from bandits to bring back a good plant.

People were amazed with what Frank brought home. Many new plants were seen here for the first time due to him. He took pictures on his travels, too. Frank loved sharing what he saw and learned. His job was not just an adventure. It was a chance to bring the world together.

1–10
11–22
23–35
36–38
39–49
50–61
62–72
73–76
77–87
88–98
99–109
110–118
119–131
132–142
143–155
156–161

**EVALUATING CODES
FOR ORAL FLUENCY**

sky   (/) words read incorrectly

blue
 ^   sky   (^) inserted word
           ( ]) after the last word

READING RATE AND ACCURACY

Total Words Read: _____

Number of Errors: _____

Number of Correct Words
Read Per Minute (WPM):   _____

Accuracy Rate: _____

(Number of Correct Words Read per
Minute ÷ Total Words Read)

READING FLUENCY

	Low	Average	High
Decoding ability	○	○	○
Pace	○	○	○
Syntax	○	○	○
Self-correction	○	○	○
Intonation	○	○	○

Record student rates on the Oral Fluency Scores pages.

Name _____ Date _____ Score _____

Storm in the Night

Vocabulary

Read each item. Fill in the bubble for the answer you think is correct.

1. If something is **drenched,** it is

   Ⓐ soaked.   Ⓒ broken.

   Ⓑ lightweight.   Ⓓ twisted.

2. Which homograph fits best in both sentences?

The windowsill _____ wet after the rain.

We put new _____ on the pool table.

   Ⓐ flat   Ⓒ will

   Ⓑ felt   Ⓓ left

3. Melvin was out on an **errand. Errand** means about the same as

   Ⓐ long vacation.   Ⓒ adventure.

   Ⓑ business meeting.   **Ⓓ short trip to do something.**

4. Feeling afraid in a storm is **natural.** In this sentence, **natural** means

   Ⓐ normal.   Ⓒ silly.

   Ⓑ embarrassing.   Ⓓ unusual.

5. Rain was **streaming** down the windows. **Streaming** means

   Ⓐ pulling.   **Ⓒ flowing.**

   Ⓑ blowing.   Ⓓ beating.

Storm in the Night (continued)

Comprehension

Read the following questions carefully. Then completely fill in the bubble of each correct answer. You may look back at the selection to find the answer to each of the questions.

1. This selection is mostly about

Ⓐ why lights go out during a storm.

Ⓑ what happens when there is a big storm.

Ⓒ why it is okay to be afraid.

Ⓓ a boy and his grandfather during a storm.

2. From the selection, you know that Grandfather

Ⓐ is a good storyteller.

Ⓑ likes getting drenched.

Ⓒ built the house.

Ⓓ planted the tree out front.

Storm in the Night (continued)

3. Grandfather compared being brave to a

Ⓐ dog.

Ⓑ cat.

Ⓒ tiger.

Ⓓ snake.

4. What brave thing did Grandfather do when he was a boy?

Ⓐ climbed a tall tree

Ⓑ looked for his dog in a storm

Ⓒ saved a friend from a lake

Ⓓ chased a man who was seven feet tall

5. What does the sentence "The storm was spent" mean?

Ⓐ The storm was scary.

Ⓑ The storm was strong.

Ⓒ The storm was over.

Ⓓ The storm was loud.

UNIT 6 **Lesson 2**

Storm in the Night (continued)

Read the following questions carefully. Use complete sentences to answer the questions. Possible answers below

6. What are some ways that Grandfather and Thomas are different?

Grandfather is big and bearded, has a deep voice, and is not afraid.

7. Why was Thomas less afraid during the storm?

Thomas was less afraid because Grandfather and Ringo were with him.

8. What made Ringo jump onto Thomas's lap?

A bolt of lightning hit a tree, knocked off a big branch, and made a loud noise.

9. What could Thomas not imagine about his grandfather?

Thomas could not imagine that Grandfather was once a small boy.

10. What happened in the selection that led Grandfather to tell a story?

A big storm caused the electricity to go out, and this led to the story.

Storm in the Night (continued)

Read the question below. Write complete sentences for your answer. Support your answer with information from the selection.

Linking to the Concepts How did Grandfather overcome his fear of storms?

_____

_____

_____

_____

_____

Read the questions below. Your answer should be based on your own experience. Write complete sentences for your answer.

Personal Response Thomas was afraid during the storm. Have you ever been afraid during a storm? What did you do to feel better?

_____

_____

_____

_____

_____

Storm in the Night (continued)

Grammar, Usage, and Mechanics

Read each question. Fill in the bubble beside the answer in each group that is correct. If none of the answers is correct, choose the last answer, "none of the above."

1. Which sentence has correct punctuation?

Ⓐ The jar had many, pennies, nickels, and dimes.

Ⓑ The jar had, many pennies nickels and dimes.

Ⓒ The jar had many pennies, nickels, and dimes.

Ⓓ none of the above

2. Which sentence has correct punctuation?

Ⓐ It's the towns only store. Ⓒ It's the towns' only store.

Ⓑ It's the town's only store. Ⓓ none of the above

3. Which sentence has a possessive pronoun?

Ⓐ Jo bought her lunch. Ⓒ They shared it.

Ⓑ She ate with friends. Ⓓ none of the above

4. Which sentence is correct?

Ⓐ The pilot said, We will land in a few minutes.

Ⓑ The pilot said "we will land in a few minutes."

Ⓒ The pilot said, "We will land in a few minutes."

Ⓓ none of the above

5. In which sentence are the plural nouns correct?

Ⓐ Birds ate the cherrys on the tree.

Ⓑ Police officers wear badges.

Ⓒ The sharp knifes are in the drawers.

Ⓓ none of the above

Storm in the Night (continued)

Analyzing the Selection

Read the question below. Write complete sentences for your answer. Support your answer with information from the selection.

What are some things that helped Thomas feel less afraid during the storm?

_____

_____

_____

_____

_____

_____

_____

_____

_____

_____

_____

Storm in the Night (continued)

Oral Fluency Assessment

Bud Goes to Teri's House

Bud said, "Mom, I'm bored."	1–5
"Why don't you walk down to the park?" said his mother.	6–16
"Can I go over to Teri's? Aunt Lynne said it's okay."	17–27
"That's a good idea. I'll call Aunt Lynne in about twenty	28–38
minutes to check up on you."	39–44
Bud grabbed his coat and hat and ran out the door and down	45–57
the steps. He waited for the light to change, looked both ways,	58–69
and crossed the street. There was always a lot of traffic on the	70–82
street outside his apartment building, and he didn't want to get	83–93
hurt by a car.	94–97
He ran into the park and followed the path that went by the	98–110
lake. Teri and her family lived on the other side of the park.	111–123
Their apartment was almost a mile away, and he didn't want to	124–135
waste time and worry his mother.	136–141
As Bud passed the lake, he saw the strangest thing. A crowd	142–153
of people was watching a movie being made. Bud watched for	154–164
a bit, and then started running down the path. If he hurried, he	165–177
would still get to Teri's apartment before his mother called.	178–187

**EVALUATING CODES
FOR ORAL FLUENCY**

sky   (/) words read incorrectly

blue

^   sky   (^) inserted word

            ( ]) after the last word

READING RATE AND ACCURACY

Total Words Read: _____

Number of Errors: _____

Number of Correct Words
Read Per Minute (WPM): _____

Accuracy Rate: _____

(Number of Correct Words Read per
Minute ÷ Total Words Read)

READING FLUENCY

	Low	Average	High
Decoding ability	○	○	○
Pace	○	○	○
Syntax	○	○	○
Self-correction	○	○	○
Intonation	○	○	○

Record student rates on the Oral Fluency Scores pages.

Name _____ **Date** _____ **Score** _____

Pueblo Storyteller

Vocabulary

Read each item. Fill in the bubble for the answer you think is correct.

1. Something **modern** is

    Ⓐ small.   Ⓒ old.

    Ⓑ large.   Ⓓ new.

2. The inflectional ending *-ing* tells you an action

    Ⓐ can not happen.

    Ⓑ is happening now.

    Ⓒ happened in the past.

    Ⓓ will happen in the future.

3. **Pueblo** is a Spanish word for "town." Houses in a **pueblo** are often made from

    Ⓐ adobe and stone.   Ⓒ iron and cement.

    Ⓑ wood and glass.   Ⓓ sticks and leaves.

4. Clay was rolled into **cylinders.** A **cylinder** is shaped like a

    Ⓐ drum.   Ⓒ book.

    Ⓑ triangle.   Ⓓ square.

5. April learned about **modeling** pottery. **Modeling** means

    Ⓐ using something.

    Ⓑ shaping something.

    Ⓒ painting something.

    Ⓓ baking something.

Pueblo Storyteller (continued)

Comprehension

Read the following questions carefully. Then completely fill in the bubble of each correct answer. You may look back at the selection to find the answer to each of the questions.

1. How did April learn to make pottery?

Ⓐ from taking a class after school

Ⓑ from her teacher at school

Ⓒ from a friend in her village

Ⓓ from her grandparents

2. The pueblo has few stories in books because

Ⓐ no one in the village tells stories.

Ⓑ the people do not have a written language.

Ⓒ the families do not want other people to hear their stories.

Ⓓ most of the stories have been forgotten.

Pueblo Storyteller (continued)

3. Why does Grandfather knead the clay?

Ⓐ to get out the sticks and pebbles

Ⓑ to add a thin white layer

Ⓒ to make it hard and stiff

Ⓓ to make it ready to shape

4. What does Grandmother do with the clay right after she makes a slab?

Ⓐ She mixes sand with the clay.

Ⓑ She pats the clay until it is smooth.

Ⓒ She curves the slab to make a cylinder.

Ⓓ She fires the pottery to make it hard.

5. The author wrote this selection in order to

Ⓐ show how a pueblo passes down traditions.

Ⓑ teach people how to make pottery.

Ⓒ explain that pueblos are built from adobe.

Ⓓ tell what a Storyteller is.

Pueblo Storyteller (continued)

Read the following questions carefully. Use complete sentences to answer the questions. Possible answers below

6. What were clay pots used for long ago?

<u>They were used for cooking, serving, and storing food, and as trade items.</u>

7. Why do the clay Storytellers have open mouths and children on their laps?

<u>They look like real storytellers, who open their mouths to pass down stories.</u>

8. What does Grandfather do first to prepare the clay?

<u>Grandfather first soaks the clay in water to make it soft.</u>

9. What does the family burn to harden the pottery?

<u>The family burns wood under a metal grate and they burn cow pies.</u>

10. What does April's grandfather do with broken pottery?

<u>He throws it into the river or returns it to the hills to give it back to the earth.</u>

Pueblo Storyteller (continued)

Read the question below. Write complete sentences for your answer. Support your answer with information from the selection.

Linking to the Concepts How is April learning about tradition when she makes pottery?

_____

_____

_____

_____

_____

Read the question below. Your answer should be based on your own experience. Write complete sentences for your answer.

Personal Response April is learning to make pottery from her grandmother. What is something you have learned to do from a person in your family?

_____

_____

_____

_____

_____

Pueblo Storyteller (continued)

Grammar, Usage, and Mechanics

Read each question. Fill in the bubble beside the answer in each group that is correct. If none of the answers is correct, choose the last answer, "none of the above."

1. Which of these is an interrogative sentence?

Ⓐ A new movie is playing.　　Ⓒ Call me before you go.

Ⓑ How will you get here?　　Ⓓ none of the above

2. Which of these is a declarative sentence?

Ⓐ When did you go?　　Ⓒ Put your books away.

Ⓑ Hurry or we'll be late!　　Ⓓ none of the above

3. In which sentence is the subject underlined?

Ⓐ The <u>nurse</u> helped my grandmother.

Ⓑ The nurse helped my <u>grandmother</u>.

Ⓒ The nurse <u>helped</u> my grandmother.

Ⓓ none of the above

4. In which sentence is the object of the verb underlined?

Ⓐ The passengers <u>carried</u> their luggage.

Ⓑ The <u>passengers</u> carried their luggage.

Ⓒ The passengers carried their <u>luggage</u>.

Ⓓ none of the above

5. Which pronoun can replace the underlined part?

<u>Dennis</u> couldn't find Beth or his sister.

Ⓐ He　　Ⓒ They

Ⓑ Them　　Ⓓ none of the above

Pueblo Storyteller (continued)

Analyzing the Selection

Read the question below. Write complete sentences for your answer. Support your answer with information from the selections.

In this unit, you read about older people helping younger people. Why is this important to both the older people and the younger people?

_____

_____

_____

_____

_____

_____

_____

_____

_____

_____

_____

_____

Pueblo Storyteller (continued)

Oral Fluency Assessment

Family Apple Days

Kate awoke early. She walked through the house and out	1–10
to the barn. Grandpa Stills was building a fire there. Kate's	11–21
parents, aunts, uncles, and cousins were still asleep.	22–29
Every year the Stills family met at the old farm. They spent	30–41
a whole day working as a team to make apple cider and apple	42–54
butter. This was the first year Kate was old enough to help. She	55–67
was excited.	68–69
By eight o'clock, everyone else was up. It was time to put	70–81
the apples in the press. Each person had a chance to turn the	82–94
crank. The press made the sweet juice. Some of the juice was	95–106
for drinking. The rest was put in an old pot.	107–116
Grandpa Stills called his family together. He handed Kate the	117–126
good luck penny. She tossed it into the pot. The juice cooked on	127–139
the fire. Sugar and sliced apples were added. As the mix boiled,	140–151
butter was added. After it cooked for a while, the apple butter	152–163
would be done.	164–166

**EVALUATING CODES
FOR ORAL FLUENCY**

sky   (/) words read incorrectly

blue

^   sky   (^) inserted word

           ( ]) after the last word

READING RATE AND ACCURACY

Total Words Read: _____

Number of Errors: _____

Number of Correct Words
Read Per Minute (WPM):   _____

Accuracy Rate: _____

(Number of Correct Words Read per
Minute ÷ Total Words Read)

READING FLUENCY

	Low	Average	High
Decoding ability	O	O	O
Pace	O	O	O
Syntax	O	O	O
Self-correction	O	O	O
Intonation	O	O	O

Record student rates on the Oral Fluency Scores pages.

Name _____ Date _____ Score _____

Johnny Appleseed

Vocabulary

Read each item. Fill in the bubble for the answer you think is correct.

1. What does the Greek root **scop** mean?

  Ⓐ touch   Ⓒ paint

  Ⓑ see   Ⓓ sing

2. If you are **exhausted,** you are

  Ⓐ busy.   Ⓒ smart.

  Ⓑ late.   Ⓓ tired.

3. People spoke **affectionately** about Johnny. **Affectionately** means

  Ⓐ loudly.   Ⓒ lovingly.

  Ⓑ carefully.   Ⓓ poorly.

4. Johnny **cleared** land for his orchards. In this selection, **cleared** means

  Ⓐ removed things from.

  Ⓑ paid for.

  Ⓒ dug deep holes in.

  Ⓓ raised animals on.

5. Johnny **survived** in the wilderness. **Survived** means

  Ⓐ planted trees.

  Ⓑ built a house.

  Ⓒ stayed alive.

  Ⓓ wandered around.

Johnny Appleseed (continued)

Comprehension

Read the following questions carefully. Then completely fill in the bubble of each correct answer. You may look back at the selection to find the answer to each of the questions.

1. From which point of view is this selection told?

Ⓐ in the first-person by a friend of Johnny

Ⓑ in the first-person by Johnny

Ⓒ in the third-person by Johnny's father

Ⓓ in the third-person by an unnamed Narrator

2. Which of these is an opinion from the selection?

Ⓐ Johnny's first years were hard.

Ⓑ Johnny was born in Massachusetts.

Ⓒ Johnny's father fought in the Revolutionary War.

Ⓓ Johnny lived near an apple orchard.

Johnny Appleseed (continued)

3. Which of these did Johnny do first?

(A) settled in Ohio after the War of 1812

(B) moved to the wilds of Indiana

(C) cleared land in the Allegheny Mountains

(D) had a tree-chopping match

4. Which of these happened after Johnny died?

(A) He was buried in California.

(B) People still told stories about him.

(C) His family continued to plant apple trees.

(D) The War of 1812 ended.

5. When he ran out of seeds, Johnny

(A) looked for seeds in the Rocky Mountains.

(B) got a bear family to help him find seeds.

(C) had to return to the East to get more.

(D) borrowed seeds from people near him.

Johnny Appleseed (continued)

Read the following questions carefully. Use complete sentences to answer the questions. Possible answers below

6. Why did Johnny move away from Ohio?

Johnny moved to Indiana because Ohio became too crowded.

7. Why were Johnny's early years hard?

His father was away at war. His mother and brother died before he was two.

8. Why did Johnny not build a house and settle down?

Johnny enjoyed living in the wilderness and loved the forest.

9. Why did Johnny want the band of men to have a tree-chopping match?

Johnny wanted the men to clear a forest so he could plant more apple trees.

10. Why do you think the winters slowed Johnny down?

It is cold and snowy in winter; it is difficult to travel and find warm shelter.

Johnny Appleseed (continued)

Read the question below. Write complete sentences for your answer. Support your answer with information from the selection.

Linking to the Concepts Why do you think that Johnny sometimes gave away his trees and seeds rather than selling them?

_____

_____

_____

_____

_____

Read the question below. Your answer should be based on your own experience. Write complete sentences for your answer.

Personal Response Johnny felt it was important to grow apple trees. What are some things that you think are important and will make the world a better place?

_____

_____

_____

_____

Johnny Appleseed (continued)

Grammar, Usage, and Mechanics

Read each question. Fill in the bubble beside the answer in each group that is correct. If none of the answers is correct, choose the last answer, "none of the above."

1. Which of these is a compound word?

- Ⓐ sunshine
- Ⓑ weather
- Ⓒ thousand
- Ⓓ none of the above

2. Which means <u>she is most tall</u>?

- Ⓐ she's tallester
- Ⓑ she'd taller
- Ⓒ she's tallest
- Ⓓ none of the above

3. Which sentence is correct?

- Ⓐ My dentist is Dr Carlson she is british.
- Ⓑ The pool closed on Sept. 14, but it will open soon.
- Ⓒ The Meeting is off April was a bad month.
- Ⓓ none of the above

4. Which sentence has correct punctuation?

- Ⓐ Yes your, socks have been washed. And dried.
- Ⓑ Yes, your socks have been washed and dried.
- Ⓒ Yes your socks, have been washed and dried.
- Ⓓ none of the above

5. In which sentence is the underlined part correct?

- Ⓐ Don't forget <u>an umbrella</u>.
- Ⓑ The hotel had <u>a ocean</u> view.
- Ⓒ The bee landed on <u>an flower</u>.
- Ⓓ none of the above

Johnny Appleseed (continued)

Analyzing the Selection

Read the questions below. Write complete sentences for your answer. Support your answer with information from the selection.

Why do you think that some people exaggerated when they talked about Johnny Appleseed? Do you think this is how legends get started? Explain your answer.

_____

_____

_____

_____

_____

_____

_____

_____

_____

_____

_____

Johnny Appleseed (continued)

Oral Fluency Assessment

The Butterfly Protects Itself

We all have seen a butterfly. They come in many colors.	1–11
Some are very large. Others are small. They look like flying	12–22
flowers. They are a wonderful part of summer. But did you	23–33
know their colors help to protect them?	34–40
Some butterflies have spots on their wings. These are called	41–50
eye spots. The eye spots are bigger than its real eyes. They fool	51–63
other animals. The animals think the butterfly is too big to eat.	64–75
The other animals will see the eye spots and go away.	76–86
Other butterflies use color as a warning. The colors warn	87–96
other animals. The colors say, "I don't taste good." The other	97–107
animals leave them be.	108–111
A third group of butterflies uses their colors to hide. They	112–122
look like flowers, bark, or leaves. Their colors make them hard	123–133
to see. The butterfly lands and it folds its wings. It looks just	134–146
like a plant! Other animals can not find it. And they can not eat	147–160
what they do not see.	161–165

**EVALUATING CODES
FOR ORAL FLUENCY**

sky   (/) words read incorrectly

blue
   ^   sky   (^) inserted word
              ( ]) after the last word

READING RATE AND ACCURACY

Total Words Read: _____

Number of Errors: _____

Number of Correct Words
Read Per Minute (WPM):   _____

Accuracy Rate: _____

(Number of Correct Words Read per
Minute ÷ Total Words Read)

READING FLUENCY

	Low	Average	High
Decoding ability	○	○	○
Pace	○	○	○
Syntax	○	○	○
Self-correction	○	○	○
Intonation	○	○	○

Record student rates on the Oral Fluency Scores pages.

Name _____ Date _____ Score _____

McBroom and the Big Wind

Vocabulary

Read each item. Fill in the bubble for the answer you think is correct.

1. Haste means moving

- Ⓐ quickly.
- Ⓑ quietly.
- Ⓒ slowly.
- Ⓓ far.

2. Which Latin root means "sea"?

- Ⓐ *ord*
- Ⓑ *san*
- Ⓒ *mar*
- Ⓓ *vor*

3. The wind **battered** at the door. This means the wind

- Ⓐ blew around the corner.
- Ⓑ pushed down from above.
- Ⓒ pushed animals through the air.
- Ⓓ hit hard over and over again.

4. The children **huddled** near the fireplace. **Huddled** means they

- Ⓐ stood there and watched.
- Ⓑ crowded close together.
- Ⓒ were blown upside down.
- Ⓓ ran as fast as they could.

5. McBroom will **deny** he's a liar. To **deny** something is to

- Ⓐ say it is not true.
- Ⓑ think it might happen.
- Ⓒ say it really happened.
- Ⓓ tell it to many people.

McBroom and the Big Wind (continued)

Comprehension

Read the following questions carefully. Then completely fill in the bubble of each correct answer. You may look back at the selection to find the answer to each of the questions.

1. All of these show that this is a tall tale and cannot be real EXCEPT

Ⓐ the nails they planted grew longer.

Ⓑ rabbits flew across the sky.

Ⓒ Melissa was baking biscuits.

Ⓓ the marbles were as big as boulders.

2. What held the children down in the wind?

Ⓐ marble boulders

Ⓑ shoes made of iron skillets

Ⓒ tying them to the clothesline

Ⓓ their mother's biscuits

McBroom and the Big Wind (continued)

3. How was the charging bear stopped?

Ⓐ McBroom hit the bear with a cannon ball.

Ⓑ The wind blew the bear from the yard.

Ⓒ The window slammed shut on the bear.

Ⓓ The bear kept jumping the clothesline.

4. How did McBroom break his leg?

Ⓐ chasing the bear

Ⓑ running after his children

Ⓒ stepping in a hole

Ⓓ falling off the roof

5. From whose point of view is this selection told?

Ⓐ McBroom's

Ⓑ Melissa's

Ⓒ the bear's

Ⓓ the wind's

McBroom and the Big Wind (continued)

Read the following questions carefully. Use complete sentences to answer the questions. Possible answers below

6. Is it true that McBroom would rather break his leg than tell a lie? Explain your answer.

No, because most of the things McBroom says cannot really be true.

7. Why does McBroom say the wind has "teeth"?

He feels the wind is like a pack of wolves snapping at their heels.

8. What two things happened when McBroom opened the window to shoot the bear?

The wind bent his gun, and the children were sucked up the chimney.

9. How did McBroom rescue his children when they blew away?

McBroom threw them a rope, and then walked home with them like balloons.

10. How does the point of view make the selection seem funnier?

It makes it seem like everything really happened; however, most of the things couldn't possibly happen.

McBroom and the Big Wind (continued)

Read the question below. Write complete sentences for your answer. Support your answer with information from the selection.

Linking to the Concepts How does the narrator make the wind seem stronger than it really is?

_____

_____

_____

_____

Read the prompt below. Your response should be based on your own experience. Write complete sentences for your response.

Personal Response McBroom likes to exaggerate. Tell about a time you exaggerated to make something sound funnier or different from what really happened.

_____

_____

_____

_____

McBroom and the Big Wind (continued)

Grammar, Usage, and Mechanics

Read each question. Fill in the bubble beside the answer in each group that is correct. If none of the answers is correct, choose the last answer, "none of the above."

1. Which sentence contains an adverb?

Ⓐ Dan broke the zipper on his coat.

Ⓑ The trip to Australia was a lot of fun.

Ⓒ The cat walked carefully across the shelf.

Ⓓ none of the above

2. Which word means about the same as rug?

Ⓐ grocery   Ⓒ divide

Ⓑ carpet   Ⓓ none of the above

3. Which word means the opposite of tight?

Ⓐ sense   Ⓒ loose

Ⓑ pause   Ⓓ none of the above

4. In which sentence do the subject and verb agree?

Ⓐ The ants walks up the wall.

Ⓑ That clock use a battery.

Ⓒ One of the trees have a bird's nest.

Ⓓ none of the above

5. Which verb is in the past tense?

Ⓐ arrived

Ⓑ arrives

Ⓒ arriving

Ⓓ none of the above

McBroom and the Big Wind (continued)

Analyzing the Selection

Read the questions below. Write complete sentences for your answer. Support your answer with information from the selections.

There are different kinds of selections in this unit. What are some of the things you enjoyed about each selection?

_____

_____

_____

_____

_____

_____

_____

_____

_____

_____

_____

_____

_____

McBroom and the Big Wind (continued)

Oral Fluency Assessment

Licorice

Some foods have odd names but taste good. Licorice is	1–10
one of them. The name comes from Latin. People spoke Latin	11–21
thousands of years ago. Even then people liked this flavor.	22–31
Licorice candy is made from the roots of the licorice plant.	32–42
Here's a surprise. The licorice plant is in the same family as the	43–55
pea plant! It has deep roots, silvery leaves, and pretty flowers.	56–66
Many people even grow it in a garden. You would never guess	67–78
that this plant is used to make candy.	79–86
The plant roots are cooked. Then they are dried and ground	87–97
into a powder. Flour and other things are added to make the	98–109
candy. Licorice powder is so sweet that sugar does not need to	110–121
be added to the candy. The candy is cooked and shaped. After	122–133
it cools, it is cut into pieces. Licorice candy is usually either	134–145
black or red. It is sometimes shaped into twists.	146–154

**EVALUATING CODES
FOR ORAL FLUENCY**

sky   (/) words read incorrectly

blue
 ^ sky   (^) inserted word
              ( ]) after the last word

READING RATE AND ACCURACY

Total Words Read: _____

Number of Errors: _____

Number of Correct Words
Read Per Minute (WPM):   _____

Accuracy Rate: _____

(Number of Correct Words Read per
Minute ÷ Total Words Read)

READING FLUENCY

	Low	Average	High
Decoding ability	○	○	○
Pace	○	○	○
Syntax	○	○	○
Self-correction	○	○	○
Intonation	○	○	○

Record student rates on the Oral Fluency Scores pages.

Name _____ Date _____ Score _____

Persuasive Writing

Writing Situation

Your favorite book or story

Audience

Your classmates

Directions for Writing

Write about your favorite book or story. It can be something you read or heard. Explain why you like the book or story. Write in a way that will make other people interested in reading it as well.

Checklist

You will earn the best score if you
- think about your favorite book or story before you start writing.
- remember that the people who read your writing might not have read the book or story.
- tell the name of the book or story and what it is about in the first paragraph.
- include reasons why you like the book or story.
- restate your opinion of the book or story in the final paragraph.
- include some ideas from the book or story you liked.
- write paragraphs that focus on related ideas.
- vary your sentences and the words you use.
- tell about the characters in the book or story.
- tell about the place where the book or story happens.

Four Point Rubrics for Persuasive Writing

	1 Point	2 Points	3 Points	4 Points
Genre				
Persuasive	Position is absent or confusing. Insufficient writing to show that criteria are met.	Position is vague or lacks clarity. Unrelated ideas or multiple positions are included.	An opening statement identifies position. Writing may develop few or more points than delineated in opening. Focus may be too broad.	Sets scope and purpose of paper in introduction. Maintains position throughout. Supports arguments. Includes effective closing.
Writing Traits				
Audience	Displays little or no sense of audience. Does not engage audience.	Displays some sense of audience.	Writes with audience in mind throughout.	Displays a strong sense of audience. Engages audience.
Focus	Topic is unclear or wanders and must be inferred. Extraneous material may be present.	Topic/position/direction is unclear and must be inferred.	Topic/position is stated and direction/ purpose is previewed and maintained. Mainly stays on topic.	Topic/position is clearly stated, previewed, and maintained throughout the paper. Topics and details are tied together with a central theme or purpose that is maintained /threaded throughout the paper.
Organization	The writing lacks coherence; organization seems haphazard and disjointed. Plan is not evident. Facts are presented randomly. No transitions are included. Beginning is weak and ending is abrupt. There is no awareness of paragraph structure or organization.	An attempt has been made to organize the writing; however, the overall structure is inconsistent or skeletal. Plan is evident but loosely structured or writer overuses a particular pattern. Writing may be a listing of facts/ideas with a weak beginning or conclusion. Transitions are awkward or nonexistent. Includes beginning use of paragraphs.	Organization is clear and coherent. Order and structure are present, but may seem formulaic. Plan is evident. Reasons for order of key concepts may be unclear. Beginning or conclusion is included but may lack impact. Transitions are present. Paragraph use is appropriate.	The organization enhances the central idea and its development. The order and structure are compelling and move the reader through the text easily. Plan is evident. Key concepts are logically sequenced. Beginning grabs attention. Conclusion adds impact. Uses a variety of transitions that enhance meaning. Uses paragraphs appropriately.
Writing Conventions				
Conventions Overall	Numerous errors in usage, grammar, spelling, capitalization, and punctuation repeatedly distract the reader and make the text difficult to read. The reader finds it difficult to focus on the message.	The writing demonstrates limited control of standard writing conventions (punctuation, spelling, capitalization, grammar, and usage). Errors sometimes impede readability.	The writing demonstrates control of standard writing conventions (punctuation, spelling, capitalization, grammar, and usage). Minor errors, while perhaps noticeable, do not impede readability.	The writing demonstrates exceptionally strong control of standard writing conventions (punctuation, spelling, capitalization, grammar, and usage) and uses them effectively to enhance communication. Errors are so few and so minor that the reader can easily skim over them.

Six Point Rubrics

Use the following rubrics to assess student writing.

6 Points

The writing is focused, purposeful, and reflects insight into the writing situation. The paper conveys a sense of completeness and wholeness with adherence to the main idea, and its organizational pattern provides for a logical progression of ideas. The support is substantial, specific, relevant, concrete, and/or illustrative. The paper demonstrates a commitment to and an involvement with the subject, clarity in presentation of ideas, and may use creative writing strategies appropriate to the purpose of the paper. The writing demonstrates a mature command of language (word choice) with freshness of expression. Sentence structure is varied, and sentences are complete except when fragments are used purposefully. Few, if any, convention errors occur in mechanics, usage, and punctuation.

5 Points

The writing focuses on the topic, and its organizational pattern provides for a progression of ideas, although some lapses may occur. The paper conveys a sense of completeness or wholeness. The support is ample. The writing demonstrates a mature command of language, including precise word choice. There is variation in sentence structure, and, with rare exceptions, sentences are complete except when fragments are used purposefully. The paper generally follows the conventions of mechanics, usage, and spelling.

4 Points

The writing is generally focused on the topic but may include extraneous or loosely related material. An organizational pattern is apparent, although some lapses may occur. The paper exhibits some sense of completeness or wholeness. The support, including word choice, is adequate, although development may be uneven. There is little variation in sentence structure, and most sentences are complete. The paper generally follows the conventions of mechanics, usage, and spelling.

3 Points

The writing is generally focused on the topic but may include extraneous or loosely related material. An organizational pattern has been attempted, but the paper may lack a sense of completeness or wholeness. Some support is included, but developemt is erratic. Word choice is adequate but may be limited, predictable, or occasionally vague. There is little, if any, variation in sentence structure. Knowledge of the conventions of mechanics and usage is usually demonstrated, and commonly used words are usually spelled correctly.

2 Points

The writing is related to the topic but includes extraneous or loosely related material. Little evidence of an organizational pattern may be demonstrated, and the paper may lack a sense of completeness or wholeness. Development of support is inadequate or illogical. Word choice is limited, inappropriate, or vague. There is little, if any, variation in sentence structure, and gross errors in sentence structure may occur. Errors in basic conventions of mechanics and usage may occur, and commonly used words may be misspelled.

1 Point

The writing may only minimally address the topic. The paper is fragmentary or incoherent listing of related ideas or sentences or both. Little, if any, development of support or an organizational pattern or both is apparent. Limited or inappropriate word choice may obscure meaning. Gross errors in sentence structure and usage may impede communication. Frequent and blatant errors may occur in the basic conventions of mechanics and usage, and commonly used words may be misspelled.

Unscorable

The paper is unscorable because
- the response is not related to what the prompt requested the student to do.
- the response is simply a rewording of the prompt
- the response is a copy of a published work.
- the student refused to write.
- the response is illegible.
- the response is incomprehensible (words are arranged in such a way that no meaning is conveyed).
- the response contains an insufficient amount of writing to determine if the student was attempting to address the prompt.

Oral Fluency Scores

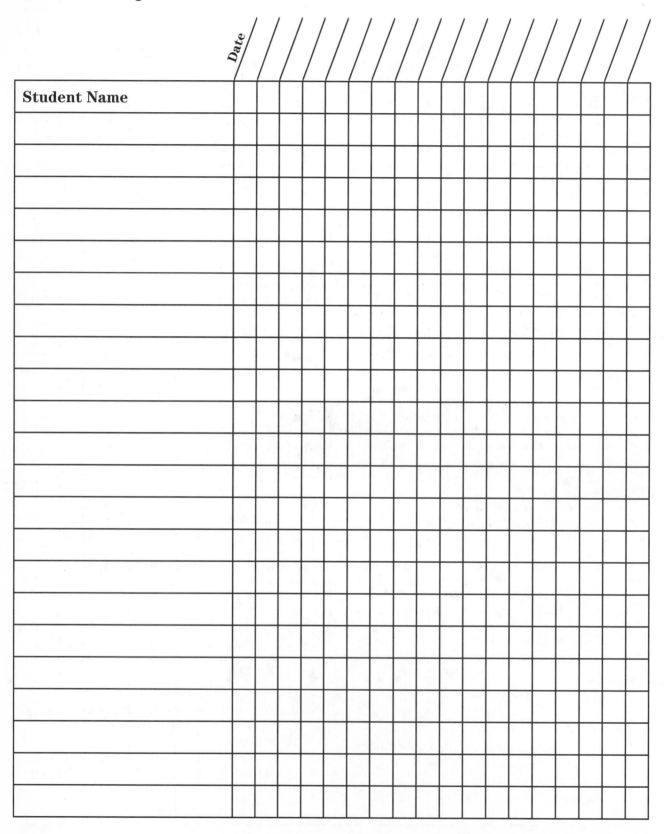

Student Name	Date															

Oral Fluency Scores

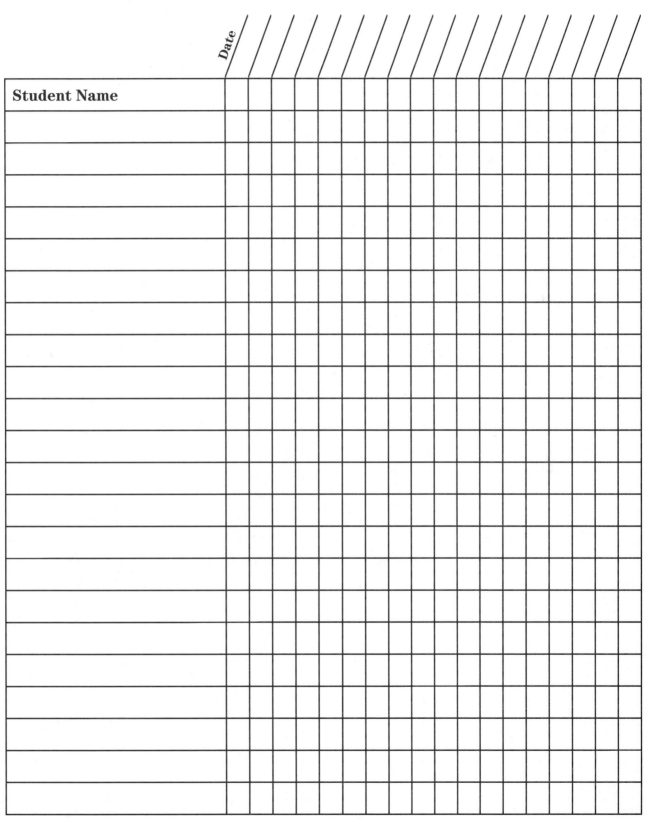

Student Name	Date																		

Class Assessment Record

Student Name	Unit 4, Lesson 1	Unit 4, Lesson 2	Unit 4, Lesson 3	Unit 4, Lesson 4	Unit 4, Lesson 5	Unit 4 Writing Prompt	Unit 5, Lesson 1	Unit 5, Lesson 2	Unit 5, Lesson 3

Class Assessment Record

Student Name	Unit 5, Lesson 4	Unit 5, Lesson 5	Unit 5 Writing Prompt	Unit 6, Lesson 1	Unit 6, Lesson 2	Unit 6, Lesson 3	Unit 6, Lesson 4	Unit 6, Lesson 5	Unit 6 Writing Prompt

Student Assessment Record

Name _____

Teacher _____ Grade _____

Unit/ Lesson	Assessment Section	Date	Number Possible	Number Right	%	Score (Rubrics/WPM)

Comprehension Observation Log

Student _____ **Date** _____

Unit _____ **Lesson** _____ **Selection Title** _____

General Comprehension

Concepts discussed: _____

_____

Behavior Within a Group

Articulates, expresses ideas: _____

_____

Joins discussions: _____

_____

Collaborates (such as *works well with other students, works alone*): _____

_____

Role in Group

Role (such as *leader, summarizer, questioner, critic, observer, non-participant*): _____

_____

Flexibility (changes roles when necessary): _____

_____

Use of Reading Strategies

Uses strategies when needed (either those taught or student's choice of strategy)/Describes strategies used:

_____

_____

_____

Changes strategies when appropriate: _____

_____

Changes Since Last Observation
_____
_____
_____